SAFARI MZURI

First published in 2006 by

WOODFIELD PUBLISHING
Bognor Regis, West Sussex, England
www.woodfieldpublishing.com

ISBN 1-84683-006-0

Safari Mzuri

(Good Journey)

*An RAF National Serviceman's
experiences in 1960's Kenya*

BRIAN J. ELLIOTT

Woodfield

Dedicated to the many National Servicemen
who served in the Middle East Air Force
and to the wonderful people of Kenya
without whose kindness this book
would not have been written.

"The one who visits you is better than
the one who sends you greetings."
Swahili proverb.

Contents

Introduction

This book is a detailed, evocative and tongue-in-cheek account of a young man's experiences whilst serving with the Royal Air Force in pre-independence Kenya.

It is based on fact, but all names have been changed to protect the innocent (as well as the guilty!).

1. *Off to Africa*

In mid-July 1959 SAC[1] Brian 'Tubs' Ryan reported to Station Headquarters at RAF Ternhill, deep in the heart of Shropshire, and officially said 'goodbye' to this world. No, he didn't die... instead a friendly and efficient Flight Sergeant steered him to Station Sick Quarters, telling him that he had been posted to RAF Eastleigh and that he was on immediate leave for one week.

Tubs was ecstatic, knowing that Eastleigh was somewhere in the proximity of Southampton. He was only too keen to get out of rural Shropshire.

On reporting to Station Sick Quarters he was impatient and having packed, was ready for the trip home on leave.

'Name?' snapped the medical orderly.

'Ryan,' came the curt reply.

'Yellow fever, cholera, typhoid and polio required. Roll up both sleeves,' the medic ordered.

'God!' Tubs exclaimed. 'I'm only going to bloody Southampton!'

The medic looked at him wistfully.

'I wish *I* was going to Kenya and out of this fucking hole.'

Tubs paled. 'What the hell are you talking about?'

'Eastleigh, mate, is in Nairobi, Kenya,' said the medic.

---

[1] Senior Aircraftsman

Tubs sat down, both sleeves rolled-up, and awaited the worst as two medics armed with fully-loaded needles bore down on him.

Seven days later he was at Stanstead Airport and twenty-three hours after that he arrived at RAF Eastleigh, Kenya and his two-year tour of duty began...

2.   *Settling In*

Tubs found the first two weeks noisy and very bruising on his shoulders. With six other new arrivals he spent two hours a day at the Ground Defence School, firing a variety of weapons and being called a variety of names by the 'Rock-Apes', as members of the infamous RAF Regiment were called. His shooting improved, as did his thirst for the local brew, Tusker.

The Khaki Drill (KD) tropical uniform fitted him well and he was beginning to enjoy life in Kenya. At night he frequented the NAAFI bar until his legs warned him of imminent collapse, whereupon he would make his way back, somewhat unsteadily, to his 'pit', climb under his 'mossie net' and pass into a coma, the last sound he heard being the incessant scraping of the crickets on the grass outside.

He passed through a lonely and spiritual stage when he took time out to watch the sunset as the Kenya sky changed in a quarter of an hour from light blue to orange, then grey and streaked with a stunning scarlet. He wrote long letters home to his parents and girlfriends in his native Chester, but with a strange air of detachment, as if they were in another world. Try as he might he could not relate to their letters or the feelings they expressed and found that many of his National Service comrades felt the same. Somehow, he could not place on paper his feelings for the wide-open spaces of his new African home. The climate was very much to his liking and he was quickly learning Swahili. Yes, Kenya was definitely the 'flavour of the month'.

After an exhaustive two weeks GD Training he found himself 'passed-out' and was told by an amicable Flight Lieutenant: 'From 0800 Monday you are Flying Wing HQ's new shorthand/typist.'

He saluted and headed, as if drawn by a magnet, to the NAAFI bar. Bedecked in his KD uniform he found himself in front of the OC Flying Wing, Wing Commander Taylor. The 'Wingco' was a pleasant man with sharp eyes who appeared to understand that many National Servicemen were keen to serve their country. He and Tubs spent a pleasant ten minutes talking about life in general and Tubs lost no time in mentioning that he would be very grateful for any 'jollies' that might be in the offing.

The Orderly Room where he spent his days was small but he felt at home in the surroundings. At nights he would catch the bus down to the New Stanley Grill and perched on a high barstool would survey the scene and sip coffee. On one particular night, he met a tall, thin man called Hardcastle, who said that he had once been a jockey, and after a few pints of Tusker they set off together to Nairobi races.

It was not long before they were amidst the hustle and bustle of the racetrack, overflowing with men from many different cultures, united in the dream of backing winners. Hardcastle was clearly well known to the regular racegoers and bookmakers waved as he passed. After the first race he began talking to a big-bosomed girl called Diana and much to

Tubs' delight introduced him to her and they began to 'talk horses' in the crowded bar. With a flourish Tubs invested £5 on a good-looking colt and to his great relief it won handsomely by five lengths.

With his new-found wealth he bought Diana and Hardcastle more drinks. Hardcastle disappeared, but quickly returned with the name of another horse in the fourth race. He was counting the bundle of banknotes he was planning to invest and seemed confident of success, so much so that Tubs doubled his wager. Soon the race was under way and as if guided by magic their selection triumphed once again, gaining the upper hand in the tightest of finishes.

Hardcastle now had rolls of high-denomination notes bulging in his pockets and with a wry smile said, 'Not a bad day eh?' He was now giving Diana the benefit of his charm with the occasional pat on the posterior and Tubs was beginning to feel like an unwanted guest. Nature called and Tubs made his way to the lavatory. It took him a little time to get through the jostling crowds and when he finally returned he was not surprised to find that Hardcastle and Diana had vanished. He never saw either of them again.

Smiling to himself philosophically he had a few more beers, gave the cheerful African barman a good tip and practising his Swahili shouted over his shoulder, 'Kwaheri Raffiki' and headed for the taxi rank.

He ended the day quite drunk but nevertheless more than happy with it.

3.   *Sun and Fun*

The Flying Wing Adjutant was a warm-hearted Flight Lieutenant called Binedall, South African by birth and an ex-
fighter pilot. Early one morning he swept through the Orderly Room and shouted,

'Ryan, do you want to go to Aden tomorrow?'

'Yes SIR!' was the quick reply, Tubs trying hard to conceal
his excitement.

'Report to Air Movements at 0700 then'.

Tubs hurried down to the Post Office, withdrew £20 and
was pleased to find that he still had a credit balance following
his successful trip to the races. At 0715 the next day he
climbed aboard a mighty Beverley of 70 Squadron and listened to the laconic drawl of the loadmaster as he went
through the 'ditching procedure'. Tubs pushed some aspirin
into his mouth to stem the pain of his hangover after another
over-indulgent night as, with a tremendous roar and swirling
of dust from the makeshift runway, the Beverley clawed its
way into the African early-morning sky.

The flight was rough, very rough, and a high percentage of
the passengers bound for Khormaksar found their way to the
chemical toilet and escaped the prying eyes of their fellow
passengers. Tubs sat and ate the awful 'in-flight meal' as the
Beverley hit downdraft after downdraft until, after eight
hours in the turbulent sky, they began to lose height and with

a bounce and squeal from the wheels the aircraft landed at Khormaksar.

An Army truck arrived to transport the passengers to Main Street and soon Tubs found himself in the commercial area of Aden. The temperature was 140 degrees in the shade; he suddenly felt a long way from home. He soon decided he did not like Aden; too many military policemen and too bloody hot. The women hid behind long black shawls, the beer was foul and the constant bartering gave him yet another head-ache. He was relieved when the MT transport arrived at the appointed time and sped at a dangerous speed back to the airfield and the awaiting aircraft.

The loadmaster had already tasted the local brew and was more than happily engaged in shouting obscenities at the Arab ground crew in Swahili, which he knew confidently that they would not understand. Had they understood they would have not been pleased! Turning into wind, after a seemingly endless wait for Air Traffic clearance, the Beverley trundled down the Khormaksar runway, wings flapping like an old duck, and lumbered into the sky, fully laden with army supplies.

Tubs fell asleep and was awakened by the easing back of the throttles and the resulting loss of height as the aircraft approached Eastleigh. When the door opened he jumped out of the aircraft smartly, running like the wind for the safety of the billet before the Customs Land Rover had time to check his case, full of duty-free cameras acquired in Main Street. He hated the Customs.

Next day the thermometer registered 105 degrees in the shade and even after the acclimatisation period Tubs found it very hot. Retreating to the Orderly Room and longing for his next drink he overhead a voice say: 'Yes, we'll organise some Hastings flights to Mombasa and take some of the chaps as ballast so that you'll get the feel of the landing with a full load.'

His ears pricked up. He had not been to Mombasa but had heard stories from those who had. They told of nubile girls, white beaches, and opportunities to enjoy both. This greatly appealed to Tubs, who had noticed that the hot climate tended to make him rather horny. He became very keen, carried out his duties quickly and efficiently and became a 'model airman' in the hope that he would be selected for the Mombasa trip.

His reward duly arrived when Flight Lieutenant Binedell appeared at the door of the Orderly Room.

'Ryan', he said in his clipped South African accent, 'We're starting some swimming trips to Mombasa on a day-return basis. Get thirty names from the register and make sure you are on the list twice a week as co-ordinator. OK?'

Tubs was ecstatic. Two days off a week! This could only be *'mzuri sana'*. Two days later the first Hastings was designated to make the Mombasa 'swimming trip'. Tubs had picked names at random, as ordered, and at dawn the following day a motley selection of airmen assembled at Air Movements, where an enthusiastic Tubs quickly marked off their names on the manifest and handed it to the waiting Air Movements

Officer. Embarkation was easy, with many of the passengers being regular flyers and totally bored with the Flight Sergeants sermon on 'the ditching drill'. The flight was smooth and the 300-odd mile trip was covered in bright sunshine in ninety minutes. Many poked at the in-flight meal and declared it, as usual, rubbish. The aircraft landed smoothly, even without the help of the regular 'trip pilot' and disembarkation was speedy, with the passengers keen to get as much out of the day as possible. An MT lorry arrived, driven by a laconic Army private who quipped: 'Wherever I drop you I'll pick you up from, but if you're too pissed I won't bother, OK?'

The lorry arrived in the centre of bustling Mombasa and Tubs climbed out, determined to enjoy his day. He walked slowly to Fort Jesus, quickly drank a couple of Tuskers to quench his thirst, took a couple of photographs and then ventured into the city centre again, armed with his street map. Tubs was now sweating profusely in the humidity and, searching for shade, stumbled on a hotel with a badly-painted sign saying 'Welcome to the New Bristol Hotel'. 'Bristol' turned out to be an apt name as girls – African, Seychelles and a combination of both – soon appeared from the fading woodwork. One passing girl whispered a sexual invitation into his ear, but he was determined not to succumb, remembering the warning words of the MO, and pushed her away, his brain still functioning despite the input of alcohol, with a polite 'hapana mzuri'.

She moved away, but not before pawing at the upper part of his thigh, causing his already alert member to stir even further. He looked at his watch; it was already 1400 hrs and the heat was oppressive and the temptations increasing. The bar appeared to be full of Seychellese girls and he soon noticed some of his fellow passengers arriving, only to disappear upstairs, arm-in-arm with a laughing girl. But he was determined not to succumb to 'the temptation of the flesh'. The Air Movements officer had briefed him simply, 'count them back on the aircraft and make sure they're not pissed'.

It was mid afternoon when a half-caste girl with long hair appeared at his elbow and smiled and giggled as he looked nonplussed through his alcoholic haze. Her skirt was cut to the thigh, showing athletic legs and a magnificent body.

'Hi,' she said, 'I'm Layla. Fancy a dance?'

He nodded as if in a dream and soon her body was pressed close to his, her arms entwined around his neck. The response was automatic. She gazed into his eyes and pouting her lips she grasped his hand and said simply, 'This way…'

At the back of the hotel they walked across a stone floor, through a door and into a room where a brightly-coloured curtain separated two beds. On reaching the bed, Layla turned and took off her blouse, exposing her greatest assets. She was proud of her breasts, which her brothers had teased her about since a young age and men had looked at with lust as she walked to and from school. She began to unbutton his shorts and he could not contain his desire any longer. He grabbed her roughly, entering her with passion, enjoying her like a hungry dog with a bone. He quickly came to an orgasm. Afterwards he looked down into the beautiful, smiling face of this radiant, happy girl, who seemed content that she had done a service so popular to members of the M.E.A.F. During the next thirty minutes it became clear to both of them that this was more than a casual meeting of a young girl and an airman a long way from home.

'Will I ever see you again?' Tears moistened her face like falling rain and her eyes sought his for an indication of the reply. Before they realised it they were making love again, caressing each other lovingly and longingly as this time she shared the moment of joy. They were an ideal match. They made love for two hours before each became aware of the premium on time. Getting dressed they gazed at each other, smiling as only the young know how.

It was only then that Tubs noticed movement on the other side of the curtain, behind which two couples were engrossed in the most passionate of lovemaking, with groans, heavy breathing and squeals of delight rending the air. He was truly impressed by the amount of animation and effort being expended.

Layla was now fully dressed and was holding his hand affectionately. He looked at her, noting again how beautiful she was, her face glowing in the light, and wondered naïvely if she was not in the wrong place at the wrong time. He kissed her passionately. An outburst of noise forced him to look over at the other side of the room. A large hairy man was dressing himself whilst a laughing African girl massaged his neck. She had huge breasts and from time to time he would playfully swing them from side to side and lick them at will. He stood up and staring at Tubs said, 'Are you on the fucking Hastings flight mate?'

'Sure am,' said Tubs.

'Well,' was the reply, 'let's get out of here and down a few beers then, OK?

Both men disappeared behind the curtain to bid farewell to their respective partners. Tubs kissed Layla passionately and she gazed into his eyes, saying softly 'Can I see you again?' He nodded.

Across the room there was again the sound of laughter and slapping and then Tubs new-found friend appeared.

'O.K. mate, let's bury some Tusker before we fly. What's your name?'

'Brian Ryan,' replied Tubs, sticking out his hand.

'Mine's Richard Bird,' was the reply, adding, with a ring of confidence 'I know Mombasa well.'

It was the start of a friendship that would last the whole of their service in Kenya, and little did they know what trouble was to come their way! They left the New Bristol high in spirits, a little exhausted but with a warm glow in their loins. Arriving at the centre of Mombasa, they sank a few bottles of Tusker while awaiting the MT lorry and Tubs was soon counting them off on the manifest and walking them out to the awaiting aircraft. Some were just happy whilst others were intoxicated but trying their best to prove otherwise, their legs drifting off course at random.

The ninety-minute flight back to base proved no problem; with clear air, none of the passengers was airsick, with the more intoxicated sleeping off their attempts to drink Mombasa dry. As darkness approached, the Hastings began its approach into Eastleigh and after a couple of bounces landed and taxied to Air Movements to disgorge its cargo.

Most were now awake, their bloodshot eyes peering through the darkness of the cabin. Dickie sauntered off to the nearby Admin Block while Tubs wearily began his one-mile walk to West Site NAAFI as he reflected on the day – it had been memorable, erotic, and yes, satisfying.

Sinking onto his 'pit', he slept well and long.

He met Dickie Bird the next day in the NAAFI. Having finished work for the day, he was quenching his thirst in a big way. They spent the rest of the day drinking, laughing, singing and generally thanking the God for their posting to Kenya and not some UK camp. Tubs wrote home faithfully every week but found it increasingly difficult to relate to events at home. They seemed a long way away and totally boring.

He arranged to meet Dickie at 1800 hours, and hailing a taxi went to see 'South Pacific' at the 20th Century cinema in central Nairobi. Across the road from the cinema they quenched their thirst before taking their seats in the circle. Suited and sporting their best ties they enjoyed the delightful, if over-sentimental musical, which proved a pleasant change from the raucous activities in the camp.

On the way back to camp, lolling in the rear of the old taxi, Dickie asked, 'How about a day in Nairobi Game Park next Saturday?'

Like many of Dickie's suggestions it seemed like a good idea at the time...

Tubs nodded enthusiastically.

4.   A Little Excursion

The plan was this. Using Tubs' UK provisional driving li-
cence they would hire a car at 0800 hours on the Saturday
and drive to Nairobi Game Park, where, armed with camera
and a large quantity of film, they would spend the day taking
photographs to send back to the UK. Searching the columns
of the *East African Standard* they came upon a hire company
situated at the rear of the New Stanley Hotel offering a cheap
day-to-day hire service. Catching the early MT transport into
Nairobi they made their way to the hire company. Its badly
scarred and crudely painted sign read 'African Roadways'.
They entered.

'Hello,' said an Asian voice with a clipped English accent,
'What can I do?'

'Need a car for the day,' said Dickie.

'Sorry, my friend but I have no cars available today.'

Dickie was stunned, but not defeated.

'What about that one?' he said, pointing to a late model
Studebaker parked outside.

'Hey, that's my personal car,' laughed the friendly Asian.

Dickie moved towards him, placing his right arm across
his shoulder.

'Raffiki, we two are returning to the UK tomorrow, and
need a car to take some animal pictures to take home to the
UK. Why not loan us your car and we'll return it tonight at
whatever time you like, OK?'

The Asian looked determined not to hire, but Dickie was in his most persuasive mood and would hear none of it. With a resigned look and a promise from Dickie that the car would be returned by 2100 hours, he finally agreed.

With a tank full of petrol and two dozen bottles of Tusker cleverly disguised as camera equipment, they finally waved 'kwaheri' to the hire-car proprietor standing resignedly on the forecourt. Tubs had never driven an automatic car before, and his experience at driving American cars was limited, to say the least. However, they set off, hope in their hearts and everything possible to them both. Tubs had mastered the gear change and they arrived at Nairobi Game Park, only a few miles from the capital, yet containing a huge selection of big game. After passing the main gate, they drew into a lay by and began to partake of the beer to stifle the heat of the day. Dickie had need of his refreshment, his throat having become parched convincing the hire company owner to loan his personal vehicle for the day.

Refreshed, they set off along the dusty tracks, which seemed to lead to nowhere. As they drove they came upon dozens of wildebeest, giraffe, gazelle and zebra and both were in their element taking shot after shot with telephoto lenses 'borrowed' via Dickie from the Station Photographic Section. Every few miles signs greeted them. 'Do not leave your Vehicle'. Lions were plentiful and both watched, with horror and amazement, a lioness stalk a Thomson's gazelle, catch it flatfooted, chase and kill it before their eyes.

After a few more hours, the Kenyan sun was turning the interior of the car into a furnace, so they stopped again to quench their thirst and eat a bunch of fresh bananas, bought from a duka at the entrance of the Game Park. They had used already a fair deal of film and, reloading their cameras, drove off in the direction of a dust-trail indicating elephant ahead. Tubs had now mastered the controls of the car, which was after all, large and heavy by UK standards.

Soon, they came across a dozen elephants busily eating acacia and in no way perturbed by the sight of the approaching American car. They drove closer and closer until the wind changed and the big bull looked at them as if to say

'That's close enough fellas.'

During their drive they came across askaris riding bicycles and this was Dickie's chance to ask in Swahili, 'Which way to the crocodile pit?' After a few minutes of gesticulating they set off, following the askari's directions.

'Take it easy, the askari says the track is none too good down here,' said Dickie, as columns of murram rose over the car. Tubs was now confident of his ability and fired with enthusiasm, free air, a sense of adventure, and not forgetting the Tusker, he began the slow, steep descent into the area of the crocodile pit.

All went well for half a mile but then the road became dramatically steeper and he became apprehensive as the speed increased and the gradient steeper. Every time he braked, great clouds of murram swept upwards and over the windscreen, making vision difficult. The wipers were of little use, then the car increased speed alarmingly, and the track became narrower. Either side of the track was a fifteen-yard high embankment. The car was no longer responding to braking but sliding and skidding, alarmingly. Both driver and passenger were becoming increasingly alarmed, their faces etched with fear.

'For Christ's sake stop the fucking thing!' Dickie shouted.

But it was too late.

Through the windscreen, Tubs saw to his horror an ultra-sharp bend around which he could not hope to negotiate in such a large car and at the ever-increasing speed.

'Hang on…' he shouted, against the roar of the V8 engine, 'I'm going up the bank.'

He flung the wheel violently to the left and the car shot upwards like a rocket, its nose heading skyward at a 40-degree angle. Quickly he disengaged the gears, switched off the engine and awaited the pull of gravity and the trip backwards down the embankment.

With a creaking, followed by a rending of metal and crashing of glass, the rear bumper hit the ground for the last time. The next few seconds were horrific as the car tilted and its occupants were treated to a slow-motion trip upside down. With a tremendous crash, the car finished resting upside-down like a wounded dinosaur, the windows shattered, glass everywhere, and the smell of petrol filling the air.

Tubs looked across at Dickie, lying upside down and moaning. Blood was flowing freely from his nose and lip.

'For Christ's sake get out you bastard!' screamed Tubs.

Survival was now important, and Dickie pulled himself out of the window and Tubs, holding a bloody right knee, followed his example. Petrol was trickling from the car onto the hot murram.

'Get clear of the car!' shouted Tubs hysterically, noticing a sign less than one hundred yards away which read, 'Do not leave your vehicle - beware of lions'.

'Christ,' thought Tubs, 'which is worse, being burnt to death, or eaten by lions?'

Dickie was now shouting at the top of his voice, pointing, as, out of the dust, appeared a Land Rover. 'God IS on our side,' thought Tubs! The Land Rover arrived with two immaculate Kenyan policemen. One got out and peered into Tubs weary, blood-spattered face and the remains of the car querying, 'Strewth, how the hell did you manage that?'

There were no witnesses except the animals, and after giving their names, Tubs and Dickie were helped into the Land Rover and at speed transported to the Sick Quarters at Eastleigh.

A state of shock was now overwhelming them both, culminating in extreme fatigue, not helped by the multiple bruising they both experienced, and in Tubs case, a deep feeling of guilt paramount in his mind. After shaking their hands, the two policemen left them at Sick Quarters.

Just before their departure, Dickie had whispered an instruction to the senior officer to advise African Roadways where the vehicle had crashed and to apologise for the damage.

The MO arrived and for a change appeared to be in a good mood. After examining Dickie, he dispatched him to his quarters with a box of painkillers, after first affixing a large plaster to his nose. Tubs was laid out on a bed and the MO ran a needle up and down his leg asking, 'Can you feel this?'

Tubs shook his head.

'Ryan,' said the MO, 'You'd better stay in overnight and I'll give you something to make you sleep.' With that, he pushed the syringe he was holding into Tubs' arm and he passed into temporary oblivion.

He woke with a start. His leg hurt and he was shaking badly. It had been a bad night. He had experienced a nightmare. He had dreamt he was not in Kenya, and there was no alcohol, no women, and he was back as an articled clerk in his native Chester.

'Thank God,' he said aloud, 'I'm alive!'

An orderly arrived, armed with a stethoscope and thermometer.

'Ryan, you are a lucky fucker. Lucky to be alive and secondly not to be in the can for exceeding the speed limit and being pissed as a fart at the same time.'

'Bollocks,' thought Tubs, but thought it best to keep his mouth shut. After a few minutes the orderly disappeared, still muttering under his breath. Tubs could remember the frightening last few minutes before the car overturned and hoped the Asian owner would understand the situation. But, on reflection, he doubted it. Time went slowly in the sick bay. With two cases of 'clap' either side he felt quite holy, but still had time to think 'there but for the grace of God go I.' He wrote home, omitting the grisly details of the crash and his confinement to SSQ.

The weather had become unbearably hot and it was on the second day of his treatment that Dickie arrived, still sporting the large plaster on his nose.

'Tubs,' he said, 'I made the mistake of going down to African Roadways to apologise. It took them two days to get the car out of the game park and when I tried to apologise on your behalf, well...' he held his hands aloft in mock horror, 'his language! I can still hear the obscenities now as I ran down the street with your 'friendly' Asian owner chasing me with a monkey wrench! Anyway, I've fixed it with the MPs – told 'em you blacked out with the heat.'

Tubs was pleased to see him and at least he seemed to have got him off being 'drunk in charge'. Dickie was in a talkative mood.

'Seems you might be in a week, my mate says. Here's your mail by the way.' One of the letters was from one of Tubs' schoolfriends, who had been posted to Aden in the Army Pay Corps and had only nine days before demob.

'Lucky bastard,' said Dickie.

'Unlucky to be in Aden,' retorted Tubs.

Dickie began to look bored, and with a wave walked at speed through the swing doors heading, if there was any certainty in this life, for the nearest bar. At the end of the ward, the orderly began doling out sleeping pills. After taking the pills, Tub had little time to reflect on his life, staring at the pastel ceiling. It began to slowly revolve and deep sleep followed almost immediately.

5.   *A View from the Top*

After a week in SSQ Tubs had become bored by the routine. Being able to walk, he was given jobs to keep him employed: emptying bedpans and making early morning tea had become the most common assignments. Writing home helped fill the time, but even this became totally 'balls-aching' after a while.

Looking out of the window one day, he spied the NAAFI van and, as the pain in his leg had almost disappeared, he sneaked gingerly down the stairs to purchase of a bar of his favourite chocolate – Kit-Kat. As he devoured the contraband, he wondered when the MO would decide to discharge him. He did not have to wait long. He was summoned to the MO's office. The MO sat behind his desk, shuffling papers, his glasses perched on the end of his ruddy nose.

'Ryan…' he said. 'You're wasting my bloody time! Get dressed and go back to your unit.'

Tubs left hurriedly, with the thought that the MO might well have seen his agility as he ran down the stairs to the NAAFI van. He packed quickly and waved cheerfully goodbye to the two 'pox' cases as he strode out.

He reported for duty next day at the Orderly Room, fully expecting a 'bollocking', but not a word was said. It was now September and he saw, to his abject horror, that a Battle of Britain parade had been listed on Station Routine Orders. He hated parades. Whilst stationed at Ternhill he had found himself on a Guard of Honour parade, complete with white gloves, white webbing, and rifle, and had hated every minute of it. He knew Dickie felt the same and decided, when typing out the nominal roll, to make an executive decision. He would simply omit their names from the parade roll.

Thus, on the day of the magnificent parade they simply climbed over the back fence and hailed a taxi into Nairobi. While the rest of the camp was marching up and down to 'The Dambusters March', they explored a Hindu Temple, finding that the smell of the sandalwood and incense had a mystifying effect on them. Although the exterior of the temple was ornate and elaborate in the extreme, the interior was modern, and essentially serene.

From the top of the temple, Nairobi lay before them like a giant carpet, resplendent with colour. The weather was, as always at this time of year, glorious, and the time flew peacefully by as they enjoyed their Kenyan experience to the full. As the sun slipped slowly from the sky, like a marzipan orange dipped in hot syrup, they sauntered over to the San Chicaye, a multi-racial bar near to the New Stanley Hotel, and quenched their thirst with a few glasses of Tusker.

Then a taxi back to Eastleigh was the order of the day, and on their return they were pleased to find that no one had missed their presence. The ruse to keep them from the invidious prospect of the parade ground had worked.

Despite their regular intake of alcohol, Tubs and Dickie were fairly fit and, religiously twice weekly they rose, albeit bleary-eyed, and ran together the whole of the perimeter track of the camp – more than six miles. They would race each other for the last half-mile, the prize being a large bottle of Tusker. Competition was always very brisk but it was Tubs who won on most occasions, much to the disgust of his lightly-framed rival Dickie.

To further test their newfound fitness they decided to climb Mount Longonet, approximately sixty miles north of Nairobi and 9,111 feet above sea-level. They had persuaded the MT Flight Sergeant that the PTO had suggested the trip, and in a gruff Scottish accent he retorted 'OK, but don't come looking for another fucking favour,' before signing the necessary docket.

They left early Sunday morning, the MT Corporal quiet, well 'hung-over' and driving the Land Rover fast among the quiet early morning traffic out of Nairobi. Soon they were at their dropping-off point and as they disembarked the Corporal shouted over the noise of the engine: 'See you bastards here at 1900 hours. Don't be late or you'll not find me here.'

They set off, both carrying small packs and water bottles, determined to make good progress before the sun reached its peak in the overcast sky. It was 105 degrees and the plan was to climb the steepest route in the shortest possible time. Both were surprised at the ease and the time in which they reached the summit. Although not requiring ropes or climbing sticks, part of the ascent was very steep and the track slippery with heavy dew in places. Exhilarated, they reach the peak. The view did indeed make the mountains of Tubs' beloved North Wales look like toadstools in comparison. They sat, their faces running with sweat, drinking beer from their flasks and soaking up their triumph.

Two thousand feet below them lay the centuries-old volcanic crater. Heavy cloud now shrouded the top of the mountain, protecting them from the fierce rays of the sun. After a two-hour rest, they began their descent, slipping and sliding down the grass track, laughing hysterically as they took it in turns to slip and fall on their posterior. As they descended, they spotted hundreds of Thompson's Gazelles and buck living on the plush grass of the slopes. Vultures looked down from the trees as they walked under them, the rancid smell of dried blood filling their nostrils as the wind changed in their direction.

Exhausted, they reached the main road and awaited the return of the Land Rover as they drank, feverishly, the last of their water and beer. Dead on time, the Land Rover's lights appeared out of the darkness. They climbed aboard, their muscles now beginning to ache.

'You've missed a shit day,' the Corporal said. 'A Hastings crashed at the end of the runway.'

Tubs froze. His billet was full of mates who were always scrounging indulgence flights to Aden on the Hastings Detachment flights...

6.   *A Trip to the Falls*

Tubs wrote to an old school friend, Dave Atkins, who was serving in the Army Pay Corps in Aden. During his time in the UK and on the pretence of attending night school, they had together indulged in the sport of under-age drinking. Their taste for Draught Bass had arrived in their early teens, and whenever Tubs saw the Bass brewery sign it brought back nostalgic memories of sore heads after happy nights spent groping young girls.

Dickie, after failing at the last ditch to scrounge a flight to Khormaksar for the weekend, had put forward the idea of hitchhiking to Thompson's Falls, some 110 miles from Nairobi. Both had heard great tales of Barry's Hotel at Thompson's Falls and duly booked a room by phone.

They had, by now, sussed out that the best place to hitch a lift was on the outbound main Nairobi road. Here they had waited an hour, sweating profusely, before an old Land Rover drew alongside, driven by a youngish, fair-haired woman, complete with two Alsatians sleeping behind a mesh barrier at the rear of the vehicle.

'Get in,' she shouted. 'Never mind the dogs.'

Her voice had a rich South African twang. They did mind the dogs, but desperately needed the lift. Dickie soon began to use his charm, trying hard to hide his furtive glances at her brown legs clad in stylish green safari shorts.

'I'm going to Barry's to meet my husband,' she said.

It was the first time for a long time that they had enjoyed female company of the white variety, and they enjoyed the trip as she chatted on, saying how she appreciated the presence of British troops in Kenya. Halfway through the trip she produced a hamper of food, beer and wine and, having been invited with a smile to 'Help yourself boys' they were only too happy to oblige. She drove on, fast and confident, murram dust at times enveloping the vehicle.

Soon they arrived at Barry's, where, after thanking their newfound female friend Marilyn for the lift, they helped enthusiastically to unload her belongings into the safety of the hotel lobby. While they were unloading the luggage a burly, bearded man arrived, introducing himself gruffly as her husband, and took her into his custody.

They booked into the hotel and were delighted to find their room overlooking the famous Falls. A log fire, sweet smelling of pine, lay in the grate, gratifying them with its warmth as the room temperature dropped and the sun went to sleep for another day.

Making their way to the bar, they encountered an assortment of French and German tourists, many of whom had come up-country from Mombasa to escape the heat and commercialism of the port and to see for themselves this relatively unspoilt area of Kenya.

For Tubs and Dickie, this was their first stay in a Kenyan hotel and they were doubly delighted when the friendly owner had charged them only half price after seeing their ID cards. They enjoyed a charcoal-grilled steak, washed down with some red wine of an unknown vintage, and then made their way to see the Falls. Coming down a very steep bank, with the Falls in the background and with the help of sign language, they had their photograph taken by a friendly German tourist from Stuttgart. It was a cool day with low cloud making it even cooler, and after savouring the view and enjoying the smell of pine from the nearby forest, they returned to the hotel.

Actor William Holden was a regular visitor here, according to the friendly barman, and he smiled as he told of Holden's exploits during his visits,

Just before the bar closed, Marilyn appeared with her husband, who insisted on buying them a drink and offering them a lift back to Nairobi the next day. Her husband had a coffee plantation at Thika and would be staying at Barry's Hotel for a few days longer on business. Dickie was pleased to hear that the dogs would not be returning but staying with him!

7.   *A Queer Episode*

Wilson airport lay a few miles south of RAF Eastleigh and boasted an odd collection of old aircraft hangars and sheds, mostly in a state of bad repair. Dickie had supplied, quite illegally, military navigation maps to a civilian pilot named David Maloney, and he, in return, had invited them to fly with him. Tubs was introduced to him in a small hut alongside the antiquated control tower.

'How're you doing,' said Maloney, somewhat laconically, adding purposefully, 'Let's get airborne.'

They were more than keen and eagerly helped him push the gleaming Cessna 172 out of the hangar. With the minimum of formalities, and with the help of the electric-start engine, they were soon taxiing to the holding area.

David Maloney was fat, in his forties and had bright red hair. He wore a pair of badly-fitting shorts, but the solid gold Rolex watch he wore on his right wrist was evidence of his affluence. With a roar from the American Lycoming engine, they were airborne and climbing steeply through low cloud over Nairobi. Below them lay the expanding city and its scorched earth.

Dickie was sitting in front and, after a while, Maloney took his hands and feet off the controls and gesticulated to him, saying, 'It's all yours…'

Tubs, huddled in the back, watched apprehensively as Dickie completed two steep turns and with a little guidance, flew the aircraft over RAF Eastleigh. After approximately forty minutes, Maloney regained control, reduced power, selected flap and performed a textbook landing back at Wilson.

'Let's go back into town and I'll buy you lunch,' he said.

They both protested, albeit half-heartedly, and Dickie whispered, 'This bastard's got more money than you and I will ever see…'

Climbing into Maloney's Mercedes, they headed for Nairobi's famous watering hole, The New Stanley Grill. On arrival, Maloney ordered steaks for all of them and, with the help of a few tumblers of whisky, began to unwind.

'You're in the RAF and I get paid by the RAF,' he said, with obvious pride.

Both were curious and almost in unison asked, 'How come?'

'I'm an expert in tropical diseases,' was the reply.

'What sort of diseases?' asked Dickie, fearing the worst.

Maloney began to laugh hysterically, tears running down his face, his fat frame swaying from side to side in the wicker chair.

'Syphilis and everything else of a similar nature!' he said.

All the camp jokes about 'the clap' came to mind as they realised they were having lunch with a 'pox-doctor'.

His laughter was as infectious as the diseases he treated and soon they were all laughing.

'I've made a lot of money out here treating you boys, and thanks to so many of you dirty little devils dipping your wicks where they don't belong I'm living off the fat of the land. The RAF hasn't got any doctors with my experience, so I'm on a very lucrative contract to treat all the cases they can't cure.'

Tubs had a gut reaction. There was something he didn't like about Maloney. He detected an inference that sex was not a natural function and those that partook were in some way sub-human.

However, Dickie was by now talking avidly about his love of Kenya and even the RAF, evidence that the free beer was taking its effect. Once in full swing, Dickie clearly could see no further than free beer, free food and free flying.

'Why don't you lads fly with me again,' said Maloney.

'We'd love to,' they replied, like a music-hall double act.

'How about tomorrow?'

'Sure thing,' said Dickie, 'but my mate's on stand-by.'

'That's OK,' said Maloney. 'You and I will fly up to Na-kuru tomorrow, and all three of us could fly up to Naivasha at the weekend.'

Dickie arranged to meet Maloney outside the New Stanley the next day. Maloney was now inebriated and slurring his words, sweat dripping from his brow onto his shorts. Tubs was certain that there was something odd about him. They stood up to go, Maloney shaking them both by the hand. His palms were sweaty and he stank of expensive cologne mixed with dust and body odour.

Waving him goodbye they boarded the MT bus filled with other inebriates returning to Eastleigh.

'I don't like him,' said Tubs, but his friend would hear none of it.

'It's only because he's a bloody pox-doctor. If he was in the St John's Ambulance Brigade you'd think him an ace guy.'

Early next morning Tubs heard Dickie leave, whistling irritatingly as he walked down the corridor on his way to fly with Maloney. Tubs spent a hectic morning in the Orderly Room, typing letter after letter, taking dictation and watching the clock as it slowly wound its way to lunchtime. Finally, it was time to leave and, mounting his trusty bike, he pedalled furiously towards the NAAFI. As he stood at the counter to order a drink, he glanced in the mirror behind the bar, and to his amazement spied Dickie sitting in a corner, clutching a large Tusker and staring at the tabletop.

'Oh,' he thought, 'Maloney mustn't have turned up.'

He pushed his way through to crowd to where Dickie sat.

'No show?'

Dickie remained silent, continuing to stare at the top of the table, then, without raising his head, he said, 'We took off for Nakaru and…' he went quiet again, but composing himself mentally, he went on, 'the bastard put his hand on my leg. He's an out-and-out fucking queer!'

Tubs didn't know what to say.

Dickie went on, seemingly eager to relate his gruesome experience in detail.

'When we got to the airfield he seemed as pleased as Punch to see me. Everyone there must have known about him. They were giving me sidelong glances. But still I hadn't twigged the real reason why he wanted to take me to Mombasa on holiday!'

Tubs tried to imagine the predicament of being in flight in a light aircraft when the pilot put his hand on your leg.

'How did you get out of it?' he asked.

'I said to him "not here",' said Dickie 'and he turned the aircraft back towards Wilson to land.'

'What happened then?'

'Well… we taxied in, he switched off the engine and then I made an executive decision…'

'What do you mean?'

'I got out as fast as I could, ran round to his side of the aircraft, opened the door, hauled him out and punched him on the nose. Then I kneed him in the balls as he went down screaming like a pig!' Dickie grinned with obvious pleasure.

'Where is he now?' asked Tubs, mentally assessing the damage his friend might have done.

'The fucker's in Nairobi West Hospital with a broken nose, and dead lucky to get away with that.'

'Nice one.' Tubs picked up his friend's empty glass and elbowed his way to the bar. He reflected that Dickie was the last person on earth he would think of as 'queer' and couldn't imagine why Maloney had mistaken him for one.

He also prayed that if he ever caught a 'dose' Maloney would not be called upon to assist in his recovery…

8. *Love on the Beach*

The flight line at No.21 Squadron was deserted except for the slim silhouette of a man working on the lower flap of a Twin Pioneer. He looked up at the two airmen walking towards him and, recognising them instantly, shouted,

'You scrounging bastards here again?'

This was a term of endearment from Flt Sgt Hawkins. He didn't like anyone flying in his aeroplanes, not even the aircrew, and especially not smooth-talking National Servicemen.

'Where it is it today then gentlemen?' he inquired, his voice loaded with sarcasm.

'We've scrounged a trip down to Mombasa, Flight,' said Dickie, with overdone respect.

'What's the matter with the Hastings flight then?' queried the ageing Flight Sergeant, 'been sick in their kites once too often?' He laughed hysterically but on regaining his dignity then said to their abject surprise. 'Step into the office for a coffee.'

Dickie knew that this would mean some typing on the side or maybe some free film from the photographic section. All governed by the age-old adage, 'You scratch my back and I'll scratch yours.'

They sat down and waited for the aircrew, and soon the two Flight Lieutenants arrived, shouting 'OK Dickie' cheerfully and relinquishing the normal formality of rank as they walked briskly towards the aircraft. The door of the aircraft had been taken off for supply dropping and they decided to leave it this way rather than spend precious time refitting it. They taxied out across the scorched earth, and with the Twin Pioneer's engines screaming at full pitch, they bounced across the grass and climbed into the sky en-route to Mombasa.

It was the day of the annual Agricultural Show at Michell Park, one of Nairobi's great social occasions. They flew low above the showground, set in surroundings of carefully preserved palm trees and grass burnt brown by the ever-present sun. Every week the worried Kenyan farmers prayed for rain. The flight was smooth at 4,000 ft and during the flight they quenched their thirsts with cans of beer kindly donated by the two pilots.

The plan was to pick up some 'bibi experience' and later in the day visit Nyali for a swim before heading back to the airport. Soon they were above Amboselli and Tsavo West Game reserves and the pilot put the aircraft into a shallow dive in order to view at close quarters the enormous amount of game feeding below them. Elephant, buck, gazelle and zebra in their hundreds could be clearly seen. Bedraggled ostriches peered skywards but the remainder of the game took little notice of the aircraft's noisy engines.

Before long the aircraft began its final approach into Mombasa and, after a turbulent descent through wind shear, the aircraft touched down and trundled towards the holding area. The two pilots quickly disembarked, their flying suits stained with sweat. One shouted. 'Be back here at 2000 hours latest.' They waved and set off on their separate ways.

Walking along the dusty road Tubs bought, after much haggling, a giant bunch of bananas known locally as 'trunks'. Each banana was as long as a man's arm, and very cheap. He fed a couple to the famous Mombasa monkeys as they appeared miraculously from nowhere tempted by the sight and smell of the bananas. Tubs loved these little monkeys. Almost eighteen inches in height, they were friendly fellows with bright eyes. After their feast of bananas, they made their way up the hill to The New Bristol Bar with Tubs full of hope that he might catch sight of Layla again. Dickie had no particular preference.

Pushing their way through the battered door of the bar, they spotted Layla, who was polishing the badly scarred top of an ancient fridge. She wore a white cotton dress, her hair was tied back in a ponytail and a red flower was set into her hair clip. Tubs crept up behind her and threw his arms around her. She turned quickly, her eyes aglow with pleasure and disbelief at the sight of him. 'Tubs!' she cried, her eyes glistening with tears. He was speechless. He gazed at her short skirt showing her legs to full advantage and a slight blush came to his face. 'And I'm very glad to see you Layla,' he said, gazing into her eyes.

Dickie was by now in deep conversation with a young Seychellese girl at the back of the bar and shouted, 'Let's go swimming!' They set off by taxi, two airmen and two Seychelles girls, one large hamper full of quickly-made sandwiches, and a good supply of canned beer. Dickie's new-found friend Rita was enjoying every minute of their hasty departure from the bar.

Within minutes they were at Nyali, where as far as the eye could see lay white sand and blue sea. They raced each other to the surf and, laughing hysterically, swam and ducked each other repeatedly, until, exhausted with their efforts, they floated mindlessly on the water. After a while, they got out of the water, ran up the beach and collapsed onto their awaiting towels to soak up the rays of the merciless sun. They had excellent tans and the sun presented no fear.

They began to partake of the packed lunch, Layla holding Tubs arm with affection. Tubs looked at her. She was a fine looking girl by any reckoning. Her legs were perfect and their length had caught his eye when first he noticed her. He had always been a 'leg man'. Her teeth gleamed in the sunlight and she smelt strongly of jasmine. He was a long way from home and it seemed the longer she held his hand the more he felt stirred by her physical presence. They lay on the beach for what seemed hours, their bodies entwined, whispering into each other's ears. It was a romantic setting with its swaying palms and the gentle roll of the surf.

Dickie, meanwhile, had been walking on the beach with Rita and they both seemed to be enjoying each other's company. She looked, Tubs thought, a great deal more refined than Dickie's usual women!

Soon it was time to return to Mombasa and the taxi-ride proved quiet, all four reflecting on how much they had enjoyed the excursion. Dickie broke the silence, announcing the obvious.

'Girls!' he exclaimed, placing his hairy arm over each of their shoulders, 'I've really enjoyed today – can we do it again soon?' Both girls looked delighted, with Layla rubbing Tubs' leg and Rita gazing into Dickie's eyes. For once Dickie was on his best behaviour and the day was not to be complicated by sex, but just two couples treading carefully through life's emotional minefield.

They stopped for a drink at the airport bar, where Layla pushed a small envelope into Tubs' hand as she kissed him fully on the lips.

'I'll see you again,' she said simply, confident in the knowledge that their relationship had blossomed. Unable to resist the temptation, he opened the envelope to find an elephant-hair bracelet, a symbol throughout Kenya of affection and friendship. He immediately placed it around his wrist.

The two girls turned and walked away whilst Tubs and Dickie awaited the return of the aircrew. They did not have to wait long and as they boarded the aircraft the Kenya sun slipped earthward, as if saluting their day's exploits. On landing at Eastleigh they encountered Flight Sergeant Hawkins, who roared, 'I hope you two clowns haven't been sick in my aircraft!'

Dickie stepped forward. 'Thanks for the trip, Flight, I thought your wife might like these as a present from us.' He brought from his pocket two perfectly carved wooden rhinos.

The Flight Sergeant was speechless. He was still shouting 'thank you, thanks again lads' as they disappeared.

'One moment,' said Dickie, 'one more thing to do.'

Marching into the crew room, he found the sunburnt pilot who had flown them that day.

'Sir, Ryan and I would like to thank you for a wonderful day out.'

'That's OK,' was the reply, 'any time we've a spare seat you're more than welcome.'

They left together, walking into the dark with Tubs reflecting to himself,

'Dickie Bird, you've got style…'

9.   *Dickie in Trouble*

By order of the Station Warrant Officer, Tubs was moved into the Flying Wing block known as West Site. It suited him fine. Dickie slept in the same billet and the only disadvantage was that it was a mere 100 yards from the landing strip and could be extremely noisy on occasions. However, the advantages outweighed by far the disadvantages; the NAAFI bar was a mere 15 stumbling yards from where they slept and within a quarter of a mile from here could be found gazelle parading majestically through the bundu. He reflected on the cold Welsh landscape of home compared with the savage and untouched beauty of the native scenery.

Dickie, in his quest for increased excitement, had taken to drinking in the NAAFI bar and then taking a late taxi to downtown Nairobi. He had quickly mastered Swahili and had tired of the usual haunts of the New Stanley Grill and The Norfolk. He enjoyed nothing better than testing his newly-found language skills in bars where English was rarely spoken. All of the bars he frequented were technically 'out of bounds' and many were listed as 'known brothels' by that most hated section of the British Army – the Military Police. It was common knowledge that the Army had the happy knack of picking the most obtuse and shortest in stature for its policemen, but Tubs knew, as did Dickie, that it was only a matter of time before he would be caught 'out of bounds' by one of the hated MPs.

Sure enough, early one morning, the light sky beckoning dawn, Tubs was rudely awakened by Dickie peering into his mosquito net, swaying and unmistakably drunk.

'Mate, the fucking MPs have just done me for being out-of-bounds,' he slurred.

'Well, were you?' asked Tubs, rubbing his eyes.

'Was I fucking ever,' he said, laughing hysterically and falling onto his bed.

By the time Tubs had walked over to him, Dickie had collapsed into a coma, a sickly smile across his face.

One of Tubs' daily duties was to compile the facts about all persons charged, and today in the course of carrying out this particular function he had occasion to encounter an Army Lance Corporal – piss and wind personified – who appeared at the door of the Orderly Room.

'Got a form 252 against an SAC Bird,' he barked pompously.

'Good for you,' replied Tubs, 'now fuck off.'

The lance corporal was speechless, and throwing the Form 252 onto the desk, stormed out. Tubs picked it up and began to read it slowly, looking for an inaccuracy that might render the charge illegal. Otherwise it would surely result in the loss of Dickie's freedom for some days. Soon his face cracked into a wicked grin, followed by a short, sharp burst of laughter.

Hurriedly, he left the Orderly Room and went off in search of Dickie to get his side of the story. He found him leaning perilously against the NAAFI bar. The story went as follows.

Having drunk more than an average amount of Tusker and feeling rather horny, Dickie had decided to get a taxi to the Equator Club. He had his best tuxedo on, a month's pay in his back pocket and was keen to have a very good time. He had bumped into a girl called Wanda, who said she was a teacher and headed for Europe next year on a residential course. They got on great. He bought her a few drinks, and then it was closing time, even at the Equator Club, and she asked him back to her place for a coffee. He was as pissed as a fart and still randy so they left in her car. They stopped at a palatial bungalow. She produced a bottle of wine and they drank this while slumped onto a large sofa, eagerly embracing one another. Suddenly there was a loud banging at the front door and a voice shouted in a strong North Country accent,

'Military Police – open the door!'

Inebriated and befuddled, Dickie had tried to get under the bed, but instead had fallen in a heap onto the stone floor. Wanda had grabbed his hand and pushed him into her wardrobe, locking him in and putting the key in her bra for safekeeping. The banging and shouting continued so she went to the door. Upon opening it, she was confronted by a short, red-faced Army Lance Corporal, full of bile and spit.

Pushing past her, he began to search the room, his manner angry and impatient. Dickie was not to be seen. He was devastated. He paced the room until he spied the battered wardrobe. Finding it locked he said, 'Give me the key?' Wanda shook her head in dissent. 'OK,' said the Corporal.

He went outside and returned with two of his colleagues. Both looked embarrassed, but with the nod from their colleague, they slowly upturned the wardrobe, and Dickie drunk, confused and in the dark, was turned turtle.

Amidst the clamour inside the wardrobe came the immortal words.

'Let me out of here you fucking bastards!'

With a combination of Dickie's weight and force, the door flew open and he fell to the floor, to be quickly handcuffed to the Army Lance Corporal. Wanda was now crying hysterically and trying to catch Dickie's hand as they pushed him through the door to the waiting Land Rover.

'See you later, Wanda,' he shouted.

'It'll be much later, darling,' added the Lance Corporal, thereby increasing Wanda's tear flow-rate.

Then, with true Army efficiency, they took him back to Eastleigh and locked him up. Some heroes!

At 0800 next morning, SAC Richard Bird was marched into the Orderly Room in front of the gleaming desk of Flt Lt Binedell. The Adjutant hated the Army Military Police intensely. In his opinion they *enjoyed* harassing airmen for being out-of-bounds. Frankly, he didn't care a bugger what his airmen got up to so long as they didn't get 'pox' and have to miss duties.

He hardly acknowledged the Lance Corporal as he smartly saluted and began to read the charge against Dickie in his droning north-country accent. When he came to the escapade with the wardrobe the adjutant had to look down at his desk to avoid laughing.

Dickie pleaded guilty; it was the only way.

'SAC Bird!' boomed the Adjutant, 'I will sentence you to the minimum three days.'

The Lance Corporal was stunned – he had felt sure his charge would get at least seven days – and his face became red when he realised that this was meant as a rebuff to his authority.

The Adjutant was already on his feet – he had had enough of the Army presence in his office. Dickie was marched out and driven by Land Rover to the Guardroom.

The same afternoon he was summoned to the Flight Sergeant and told to return to work immediately but not to leave camp for the three days of his sentence. The Flying Wing Flight Sergeant appeared more than interested in the name of the Army Lance Corporal who had charged Dickie.

'His name is Robinson,' said Tubs.

The veteran Flight Sergeant looked up from his desk; years of RAF training had made him cunning and devious to the core.

'OK...' he said, 'We'll have that fucking bastard!'

10. Another Climb

Now was the tedious time of the 'long rains'. It rained continuously and with much more power than many in the camp had ever seen. The monsoon ditches, two and a half feet deep, were soon full to overflowing. Tubs had been assigned to 'bus escort' for the duration of the week. One week a year all airman were detailed for this duty, which entailed forming part of an armed guard to escort children from service families to and from school. It was not a task that anyone looked forward to; the children tended to be precocious, having travelled extensively with their parents, and would compete with one another in making rude remarks in the general direction of the reluctant armed guard posted at the front of the bus for their protection.

At least there was some cause for cheer. Christmas loomed near and there was a rumour going round that the NAAFI had decided to sell all alcohol without profit during this period. After his charge for being out of bounds, Dickie had become somewhat quiet and seldom left the camp at night. However, he drank with renewed vigour at the NAAFI bar and was more often than not incapable of doing anything more than collapsing in a coma onto his 'pit' at the end of most evenings. But he had begun to plan a further expedition, and without Tubs' knowledge had booked a Land Rover to travel to the nearby Aberdares to climb Mount Kinangop. It was supposedly an easy climb.

Books had also become part of Dickie's life and his fervent desire to learn Swahili had led him to a greater awareness of the political implications behind the presence of the British armed forces in Kenya. After all, Kenya was still a Crown Colony and they represented the colonial government. Jomo Kenyatta was in prison but Dickie thought it only a matter of time before Kenya was given back to its own people. Wisely, he kept his thoughts to himself.

A few days later, they arrived at MT to collect their transport for the Kinangop trip.

'Christ, not you again!' said the duty Corporal, his overall as always thick with grease. 'Get in.'

He slammed his foot hard down to the boards and the vehicle rocketed forward in a sea of dust. After forty-five minutes he slowed and they clambered out, backpacked and full of enthusiasm. The driver glanced in his mirror and shouted above the roar of the engine, 'See you tonight then!'

They crossed the road and set off towards Mount Kinangop, two lone figures silhouetted against the expanse of the sky. Climbing was not too difficult, as the slope was not too steep, but the fierce rays of the sun bore down on them mercilessly, forcing them to rummage in their backpacks to recover their bush-hats. About half way up they encountered two dozen elephant, happily eating acacia, totally unaware of the two interlopers.

It was a good day and both were at peace with the world. Hot and exhausted they reached the peak shortly after 1400 hours and sat down to eat their packed lunches, yet another culinary delight from the Airman's Mess, containing ham sandwiches, jelly, and the mandatory two oranges.

They ate with enthusiasm, having forsaken the early morning breakfast for an extra hour in bed. They began the descent with hardly a word passing between them, both in a trance-like state of fascination with the beauty of their surroundings, enjoying the total peace that was Kenya.

It was only when they reached the road that Dickie remarked, "That was a piece of cake. We must be getting fitter!'

'Maybe,' replied Tubs, 'but I'm parched. Let's find a duka and have a beer.'

They walked on down until they spied the duka, Indian-owned, as usual.

'Two large Tuskers raffiki,' said Dickie, wiping some of the sweat and dust from his forehead. They looked around. Following them for the last half a mile had been two 'mtotos', small smiling African children, the whites of their eyes stretched with amazement at the sight of the white men who had entered their domain. Magically, this number had increased to a dozen, each one nudging the other, smiling and laughing, as if waiting for something to happen. Tubs was fascinated by their interest. It was as if they had never seen white men such as them, no big car, and no guns to protect them if attacked. Suddenly he had an idea.

'Give them all a Fanta,' he shouted to the young Indian behind the counter, pointing to the ever-increasing group of children.

'No, I'll get rid of them for you,' he said, moving towards the group and throwing up his arms in a threatening manner.

'No, no,' shouted Tubs, moving between the Indian and the children so as not to scare them further. How could he spoil their day? The children were happy. This was their country and he and his friend were just passing through. The young Indian retreated with a resigned wave of his hand and began handing out the ice-cold bottles of Fanta to the eagerly awaiting children. They guzzled their fizzy drinks, their eyes agog, their faces contented. Dickie ordered two more Tuskers, which disappeared with incredible speed down his gullet. It was time to leave. Dickie paid the Indian, shook his hand, and wished him well in the future. The African children waved and Tubs patted each of them on the head as a sign of affection. It was a simple gesture but for some reason moved a muscle close to his heart and made him feel humble, if not a little sad.

They walked back to the road and awaited the arrival of their transport back to Eastleigh. They did not have to wait long and for once the MT driver was in good humour, both of them concluding that he had spent some time at the NAAFI bar before collecting his vehicle.

He drove at a blistering speed until the camp lights loomed into sight. They tumbled out and quickly unloaded their gear, shouting 'thanks mate!'

'My pleasure,' was the driver's laconic reply, as the Land Rover shot forward as if rocket-propelled.

They made their way to the billet, tired but happy. After a quick cold shower to flush the dust and sweat from their aching bodies, they sank into their 'pits'.

'Why don't we climb Kilimanjaro?' said Tubs. 'That would be something to remember.'

But both had heard tales of acute headaches, altitude sickness and broken limbs from those who had attempted the climb.

'Bugger off!' said Dickie, before passing into deep sleep, and filling the billet with the noise of his snoring.

11. *Fun in the Air*

Flight Lieutenant Binedell, the Flying Wing Adjutant, was a frustrated desk-bound ex-fighter pilot. South African by birth and quite rightly proud of it, he had flown in World War Two and was court-martialled, so the story goes, after flying a Spitfire at treetop height over a train taking pacifists to a local peace rally. Reinstated as a flyer he had won the DFC. He was a good-tempered man with a broad view of life and all who met him respected him, none more than Tubs.

To qualify for his precious flying pay he had to fly a given number of hours each month and to do this he took to flying Station Flight's only Chipmunk. The Chipmunk was a monoplane, well proven for training ham-fisted pilots, and a joy to fly for the professional pilot. The Adjutant appeared early one day, clad in his blue flying suit, bone-domed, and looking in a hurry to do what he did best; fly.

'Ryan, want to come flying?' he shouted, his voice earnest and keen.

'Love to, Sir,' was the quick reply.

Tales had circulated throughout the station of his flying, illegal low flying at times some said, but never proven.

'Get this on,' said the Flight Lieutenant, throwing a well-used flying suit at Tubs. Station Flight was a short walk and Tubs almost had to run to keep up with the long strides of the Adjutant. The Flight Sergeant i/c sprang to attention as the Adjutant walked towards him.

'Chipmunk, ready to go?' asked the Adjutant.

'No problem Sir' was the Flight Sergeant's smart reply, knowing only too well that if there had been a problem, World War 3 would have broken out there and then!

Both pilot and passenger were fitted out with the customary parachutes. Two burly Corporals strapped Tubs into his chute, pulling hard on the restraining cords so that he could not stand upright. Parachutes duly fitted, they made their way to the aircraft, looking like two stooping monkeys, the parachute hanging heavily on their backs. Locked in the rear seat the Adjutant did his pre-flight checks, fast and precise after years of practise.

'OK Ryan?' he shouted above the roar of the engine.

'Yes sir,' replied Tubs.

'If we have to bale out, I'll roll the aircraft, ditch the canopy and then all you have to do is to hit the release catch and you'll fall out,' said Binedell, his South African drawl becoming muffled over the intercom.

Turning onto the main runway, the little monoplane trundled forward as if keen to fly, and with seemingly little effort they were airborne.

'We'll fly down the escarpment and look for some game.'

'Thank you,' replied Tubs, wondering at his luck.

Banking sharply, the Adjutant turned the aircraft in line with the main Nairobi road and headed towards the escarpment, where, without doubt, some thousands of feet down, feeding on the floor of the escarpment, there would be an abundance of game.

'Hang on, we're coming up to the escarpment,' drawled the pilot. On hitting the hot air, the aircraft rose like a high-speed lift and for a few minutes bucked wildly, engine screaming and wings swaying. When the turbulence settled, the pilot pushed the stick forward and dived towards the plains covered with dots, which quickly revealed themselves to be big game – elephant, zebra and wildebeest.

Not satisfied with the view, the Adjutant dived again to within fifty feet of the ground and began to chase a herd of zebra. The herd seemed unafraid and just looked up as if in amazement at the metal bird that had invaded their privacy.

For fifteen minutes the Flight Lieutenant flew his aircraft fast and low, reliving his days as a fighter pilot, and then began to climb.

'Ryan, it's my son's birthday,' his voice crackled over the intercom, 'so we're going over to the house and when I raise my left hand I'll do a barrel roll, OK?'

Tubs did not have to wait long. Over the port wing there soon appeared a large house with a group of people standing in its enormous garden. The Adj's left hand shot into the air and immediately the power was increased and the aircraft, within the space of a second, rolled over and over.

'OK Ryan?' the Adjutant laughed into his intercom.

Before Tubs had time to reply, the aircraft rolled again, and this time to port.

'Fancy, a waggle with the joystick?' asked the happy pilot. Again, before he could reply, Tubs felt the controls go slack as the Adjutant released his control. Tubs quickly placed his feet on the rudder pedals and calmly put his hand on the joystick.

'Take it up to 6,000,' ordered the Adjutant.

Tubs pulled the stick gently back and the aircraft climbed rapidly until just short of 6,000 feet. He eased the stick to neutral again, the trimmed flying control now steady.

'OK,' said the pilot, 'Now take it down to 2,500 feet.'

Tubs was ecstatic. This would be something to tell those admin buggers when he got back!

At 2,500 feet the now remote voice from the front said, 'You're dead in line to land, keep taking it down until I say 'I have control' then take your feet and hands off fast.'

They continued on down, the ground looming larger by the second, the wings moving slightly in the turbulent air, and the wind shear affecting Tubs' tender handling.

He looked at the altimeter. It read 500ft. He took another look. It read 150ft … and still no response from the voice in front. Tubs began to sweat. At 100ft, to his relief, there was a crackle and the laughing voice of the Adjutant, shouting 'I have control!' and seconds later with a bump and rattle from the wheels they were back on the ground.

They taxied in at running speed for a fit man, the Adjutant in a hurry to get back to his desk. 'You did really well there Ryan,' he said, sounding sincere and enthusiastic. 'Next time, I'll let you do the take-off. It's a piece of cake!'

By the time Tubs had climbed out of the back seat the Adjutant had gone. He could just be seen in the distance, his long legs eating up the ground on his way back to the Orderly Room.

'Everything OK?' asked the Station Flight Corporal, retrieving Tubs' bone-dome and parachute. 'Oh, and by the way,' he added, with a tone mock seriousness, 'if at any time the parachute doesn't work, don't be afraid to bring it back.'

Tubs could still hear the corporal's cackling laughter as he closed the metal door of the hangar and headed back to his duties.

12. *Opportunity Knocks*

Life proceeded at a slow pace in the Orderly Room, the only available excitement being generated by reading the charge forms as they came in for processing. Dickie continued in his efforts to drink Kenya dry but took to innocent pursuits like visiting the Station Cinema, leaving his colleagues wondering whether he was pining for something.

One of the more cynical forms of station sport was the posting of 'Dear John' letters on the NAAFI notice board by their recipients. Almost everyone posted to Eastleigh who had once boasted a UK girlfriend eventually received a letter advising him that she was married, engaged, going out with another, or otherwise enjoying her sex life elsewhere. Life at Eastleigh, however, continued without any suicides, perhaps just a little heavier drinking by the serviceman concerned.

White girls in Kenya were at an absolute premium and to mention that you were in the RAF was the absolute 'kiss of death' due to the bad local reputation of sex-starved airmen and the sexually transmitted diseases they carried.

It was Tubs' misfortune to suffer from an attack of piles, forcing him to visit the MO. He made the mistake of writing to his mother advising her of his complaint. She wrote back quickly, telling him not to sit on damp walls! Also contained in the letter was the sad news that one of his former girl-friends had moved away. He mentally crossed her name off his Christmas-card list.

He had noticed that Dickie had become furtive recently, a bad sign. He had become very keen in his work, sorting out maps for incoming aircrew, and it was obvious that something was afoot. Apart from this, he had taken to writing long letters home and reading English papers stolen from the crew room.

On the 24 November 1960 at 0750 the Adjutant arrived at his office shouting as he walked through the door, 'Ryan, get in here!'

Tubs had a horrible feeling that he was about to be posted to Aden. Rumours were rife of a shortage of personnel at Khormaksar. He shot through the door.

'Sir?' he queried.

'You and your friend SAC Bird,' spluttered the Adj. 'I've just gone and sold my soul to get you both on a Rhodesian DC-4 coming through tonight on the way to the UK. Both of you have to be at Air Movements tonight at midnight to catch this indulgence flight, but you should be able to get a ride back with the Britannia Detachment flight.'

Tubs looked at his boss, not knowing whether to laugh or to cry. His only thought was how long it would take to strangle Dickie, for without doubt, he had known that this flight was scheduled a few weeks ago. He ran round to the Air Traffic building and found Dickie leaning nonchalantly against his map board and, as always, writing away with his blue chinagraph.

'You bastard, we're going to the UK tonight and you knew all along.'

'No way!' was the reply, Dickie appearing genuinely excited, if not surprised.

There was no time to argue, as they had to clear the station, get countless forms signed, and pack.

'Pack what?' thought Tubs. He had given away all his heavy clothing to the dhobi boy, who would no doubt have sold it by now. He reflected that it might even be snowing in the UK. Excitedly, they packed together, with Dickie loaning some of his heavy clothing.

Air Movements was a five-minute walk from the billet and suddenly they found themselves in a happier mood as the spirit of adventure rose within them, and they set forth to the NAAFI bar.

For reasons of security there was no way of telling their parents of their impending flight before they reached the UK, but once again the RAF felt like a good place to be.

13. On route for England

Their arrival at Air Movements was marred by the antics of the duty Air Movements Officer, a red-faced Flight Lieutenant who hated Kenya with a passion, hated the RAF and rumour had it that his wife hated him also. It was he who now confronted them. On seeing them his face turned white with rage.

'Where the fucking hell have you been? You should have reported here at 2030 hours!' he stormed.

It was now 2320 hours.

Dickie quickly took control of the situation, knowing the Air Movements Officer of old as a commissioned bully.

'Sorry sir, but the SATCO definitely told us both to be here by midnight at the latest,' adding quickly, 'Sorry if we've inconvenienced you.' At this, the officer seemed to calm down and simply queried, 'Much baggage chaps?'

'Just these two bags,' was the quick reply, 'and they'll go under the seats.'

The Flight Lieutenant was still red-faced and pacing the floor like an impatient bulldog. He wore a brass-buttoned tunic and long trousers instead of the customary tropical kit of lightweight tunic and shorts.

Also on the flight were two Army privates who had arrived with a load of excess luggage much to the displeasure of the AMO. They stood in a corner, sulking from the venom of his words. Out of the darkness came the lorry destined to take them to Embakasi airport, all passengers helping the driver to load, keen to get on their way. With customary speed, the vehicle was on its way, tyres screaming at every corner, and it was not long before the impressive facade of the airport building came in sight, hiding the administrative chaos within.

The DC-4 passengers were ushered to a small lounge bar where passports were collected by a Rhodesian Air Force Flight Lieutenant with a deep and impressive tan, his hair scorched blonde by the sun. There was an air of pre-flight jollification, with all the passengers taking advantage of the duty-free bar, and before long the Rhodesian Flight Lieutenant returned their passports with a smile. Tubs had time to look through the lounge window and see a DC-4 aircraft, gleaming as new, being loaded for its long journey north. The main doors were lined with stainless steel, as were the propeller domes, and a freshly-painted pair of steps loaned from BOAC completed the picture of efficiency.

Uncharacteristically, Dickie and Tubs were drinking whisky, a liquid which, according to the MO, 'whilst flying prevents frequent visits to the toilet and induces sleep'. After all, he should know, he drank bottles of the stuff himself on a regular basis.

Soon, the ever-smiling Flight Lieutenant appeared and beckoned them to follow him, across the runway to the awaiting big bird. The aircraft had been separated into three sections, with the large centre for the Rhodesian Air Force senior officers and their staff, complete with wardrobes, tables, and washroom, and the rear for the small number of passengers. The interior was immaculate and had been freshly sprayed with expensive deodorant; a far cry from the interiors of their usual transport, the trusted Beverley, with its constant smell of oil and the body odour of its passengers.

Their first stop would be El Adem, and with a crack and rumble from the American engines, the aircraft taxied out and with previous clearance from ATC was soon airborne and climbing steadily to its cruising altitude. The cabin lights were extinguished and, aided by the whisky, Tubs and Dickie fell into a deep sleep with dreams of good times ahead in the UK.

The next noise Tubs heard was the sound of the wheels being lowered in preparation for landing at El Adem, and all the passengers looked forward to stretching their legs on North African soil.

But it was not to be. On landing, the aircraft taxied to dispersal where steps were quickly placed in position and a bearded man wearing a garish uniform boarded and took away all the passports and the passenger manifest. It became apparent that the only person allowed to leave the aircraft was the captain, to supervise the refuelling of the aircraft. The heat in the cabin soon became unbearable and sweat poured from their faces, staining their newly-acquired civilian shirts.

The captain was furious and, after uttering a few well-chosen Anglo-Saxon words as he reclaimed the passports, quickly took off for the second leg of the flight to Luqa.

In order to alleviate the boredom and stretch their legs
Tubs and Dickie offered to help the catering staff in the small
galley. The flight sergeant and corporal, both Rhodesian
born, were making their first trip to the UK, and were now
being teased mercilessly on how cold it would be in London
compared with their home town of Salisbury.

It was a four-hour flight to Luqa, boring in its smoothness,
and with the low drone of the engines Tubs and Dickie were
both soon asleep again.

On the approach into Luqa – power off, flaps down – Tubs
noticed that along either side of the runway, at approximately
150-yard intervals, stood immaculately-uniformed Military
Police, standing to attention and saluting smartly. It was then
he realised that they were aboard a truly VIP flight.

The aircraft landed, the VIPs disembarked and, after what
seemed a lifetime, the other passengers were ushered down
the steps into the darkness of Malta's one and only airport. A
Corporal said, 'Welcome to Malta, lads, you're in the transit
billet and your bedding is on your pits.'

The plan was simple. Have a meal in the NAAFI, a few
beers and then head downtown for the infamous 'Gut' or
'Strait Street', as the guidebooks called it. They ate the Maltese interpretation of steak and chips with relish and headed
for the main gate and the waiting line of taxis.

The ride to Valletta was memorable, to say the least. Not
being religious, neither Tubs or Dickie could understand
why a large cross and a picture of the driver's family was
hanging on display in the front of the taxi. However, it soon

became apparent that this might be the last thing they ever saw, given the pace at which they were travelling. Accompanied by the smell of burning rubber at every corner and at a speed well in advance of a Chipmunk's take-off velocity, they were propelled into Valletta, as opposed to being driven – flung around like a pair of rag dolls on the taxi's back seat with each abrupt change of direction. At last they stopped at the top end of the Strait.

'Thanks for the drive,' Dickie said, breathlessly, 'all I have to do now is change my underpants!'

The driver looked puzzled but grateful for his tip.

It was 2230 Maltese time and life had begun in earnest in the many bars of downtown Valletta. At the door of every bar stood girls with winning smiles and a short skirts, most hardly out of their teens, each extolling the pleasures to be had inside. It was a hard sell but they had heard it many times before. Maybe drunken sailors might fall for it, but wide-awake airmen rarely did. They walked the whole length of 'the Gut', picking out the more interesting places, and met four giant American MPs. One, tall and overweight, who went by the name of Hank, said, 'Get your ass down to the *Galvanised Donkey* – that'll seal your night, Buddy!'

So after buying them a drink and a cheery 'See ya guys' Tubs and Dickie made off in the direction of this curiously-named watering hole.

It was now late evening and the Galvanised Donkey was heaving with matelots. The bar was adorned with the cap badge of almost every ship in the world and the counter was awash with beer overflowing onto the sawdust-scattered floorboards. Fighting his way through the drunken throng Dickie ordered the mandatory beer and looked around.

Everywhere he looked there were hairy young men sitting or standing, many of them swaying, glass in hand, some even attempting to sing. Most of those seated were enjoying the attentions of young Maltese girls, displaying ample cleavage and ready smiles.

On the stroke of midnight, without any warning, all the lights went out and in a makeshift spotlight stood a Maltese girl wearing a mask and heavy make-up. This, they imagined, was the cabaret.

Without any finesse she undid the top of her blouse, revealing a pair of floppy breasts and, taking a bottle of baby oil, began to rub her breasts in a suggestive manner, the oil glistening on her large nipples. Urged on by the baying, stamping crowd, she took off her skirt and, as the catcalling reached fever pitch, removed her black knickers and paraded along the top of the bar, just out of reach of the eager hands of her rowdy audience.

With a theatrical flourish, she reached down to one of the drinkers, took his bottle of Guinness, poured it over herself and began to lick the liquid from her breasts. The audience were now going wild, some leaping onto tables to find a better view. One or two of the more inebriated could not stand the excitement and disappeared with a thud.

The Guinness bottle now empty, with a lick of her lips she slowly inserted the neck of the bottle into her vagina, and walked slowly and teasingly the length of the bar for all to see. Then, with a violent gyration of her lower abdomen and a terrific roar of encouragement from the now riotous crowd, she propelled the bottle into the air and towards the back of the room. Soon she was accepting more eagerly proffered bottles, which she duly propelled, by similar means and with surprising accuracy, back into their owner's hands.

The bar was in an uproar, and fearing that this amount of noise would alert the MPs, Tubs and Dickie left. At the door Dickie, somewhat aroused by the performance, could not resist groping and French-kissing the girl at the entrance, before staggering out onto the cobbled street.

A young Maltese boy approached, carrying a tray full of watches and lighters and it was time to barter. Dickie bought a watch for his sister and Tubs, after much haggling, a cigarette lighter that played 'Drink to Me Only with Thine Eyes' for his mother. They rolled up the street together, tired but happy, towards the taxi rank.

The taxi-ride back to camp was more restrained than the outward trip, perhaps due to the driver's fear of them both being sick. On arrival they quickly collapsed onto their beds and the last thing Tubs remembered was Dickie saying,

'I wonder why she only uses Guinness bottles?'

14. *Last Leg*

Tubs awoke with a start. A fat MP stood over his bed with a torch and a wild-eyed Alsatian dog at his side. 'Get up you dozy bastard, you're flying at 0600,' he said. Tubs looked at his watch, it was 0500. Dickie was already dressed, the MP having called on him first. He had already made the decision to forego breakfast, as he was none too sure he could keep it down. Still tired and disorientated, they made their way to Air Movements clutching their UK-bound baggage.

The Rhodesian Flight Lieutenant was manning the desk.

'Had a good night?' he asked, eying them sympathetically. Without further ado, they were led out to the awaiting aircraft and it soon trundled out and took off, heading north once again. Tubs was just slipping into a deep sleep when he was startled by a voice inquiring, 'Are you SAC Ryan who hails from Liverpool? He looked up to see a middle-aged, heavily tanned man slouching over the rear of his seat.

'Well... I come from Chester, near Liverpool, and my name's Ryan. Friends call me Tubs.'

'I live up there too and I thought you might like a lift.'

The thought of getting home without the hassle of catching a train appealed to Tubs immensely, so he agreed enthusiastically.

'OK,' said his new-found travelling companion, 'see you when we disembark at Stanstead.'

The drone of the piston engines soon sent them into blissful sleep, each dreaming of what lay in store for them in the UK. On awakening, Tubs detected activity among the passengers, few as they were, who had begun to wash and shave prior to landing. He sat quietly for a few minutes, wondering whether, after fifteen months, anybody back home, apart from his parents, would remember him.

With a clunk, the undercarriage wheels locked into place, the landing light came on, and slowly, awkwardly, the DC-4 descended through heavy rain and fog into Stanstead Airport, UK. It was some time before they were allowed to disembark and Dickie began to explain how they were getting back to Nairobi via RAF Abingdon on a Beverley flight. Detachments had a nasty habit of being moved overnight leaving 'free-loading' passengers high and dry. They exchanged addresses and telephone numbers, carefully checking details as if it was a secret military operation. Finally they were allowed to disembark and Tubs was delighted to spot his new-found friend happily waving a set of Hertz car-hire keys and keen to go.

'Just got to make one phone call, Bill… only take a minute,' shouted Tubs, scurrying off towards the phone booths at the end of the customs hall. It was 2330 local time. He rang the Chester number, and after waiting for what seemed ages, he heard his father's gruff 'Hello', indicating that he was displeased at the lateness of the call.

'It's me Dad. I'm in England and I'll be home in about four hours,' said Tubs cheerfully.

'Christ!' said his father in amazement, followed immediately by the phrase hated by all National Servicemen. 'When do you go back?'

Tubs was speechless. Replacing the receiver he walked back to Bill and the awaiting transport. He felt disconsolate looking at the steady rain and fog that awaited them.

Was he 'home'?

He was none too sure.

15. *Heading North*

Together Bill and Tubs set off, heading north, weary after their long flight. Tubs found himself landed with the job of navigator and lost his way on numerous occasions, directing them down every 'B' road imaginable. After two hours of driving in ceaseless precipitation, Bill had had enough, and said so in no uncertain terms and he turned off into a roadside café car park.

Tubs cast his critical eye over the typical 50s-style café, offering a minimum of comfort, a menu of items deep-fried in dark oil, and a questionable standard of hygiene. Bill ordered a mixed grill and upon its arrival it was not long before he made his first culinary appraisal.

'This is fucking awful!' he said, toying with the burnt remains of a sausage.

Tubs had ordered egg and chips and having dutifully smothered it with tomato ketchup, decided it was at least hot and edible.

Bill was beginning to feel the cold. Not having been in the UK for twenty years, his system was no longer equipped for the wintry dampness that was now enveloping him.

'Where's the bar, mate?' he inquired of a long-haired youth slouching against the grill wall. The youth motioned, with a heavily nicotine-stained finger, to a badly lit area of the room where, through the gloom, could be seen a small assortment of bottles and optics.

'For Christ's sake, let's have a drink,' said Bill, throwing his knife and fork onto his plate with resignation. The youth sauntered over to the bar in readiness for their order.

'Two very large scotches, please,' said Bill. They drank eagerly to stave off the cold. The youth inquired, after looking at Bill and noticing his deeply-tanned features, where they had come from.

'Kenya and Rhodesia,' replied Bill.

The youth nodded, his face blank, not in the least interested in continuing the conversation.

Having finished his drink, Bill began to shake with cold.

'Same again,' said Tubs, sparking the barman into life. They were beginning to enjoy the whisky, which warmed their stomachs and brought a glow to their faces. Then it was time to go. With a 'see you' from them and a grunt from the barman they stepped out once more into the darkness and rain.

After another hour's driving they spotted a sign saying 'Chester 28 miles'. They drove on along the 'B' roads and twisting lanes that laced their way through Cheshire like spaghetti. Soon, they arrived at the Warrington bypass and Tubs, realising that he would soon be home, for the first time since arriving in the UK, felt excited.

On reaching Chester the sky cleared and soon their hired car was making its way into Cambrian Avenue, which, for most of his life, Tubs had known as home. His father stood at the door of the house supporting his mother, who looked happy but tearful.

Tubs jumped out of the car, shook Bill's hand firmly and gave him his telephone number to confirm the trip back to Stanstead. With much horn blowing, the car accelerated into the darkness.

Tubs ran towards the porch of the house, his hand out-stretched to his father, who looked amazed and pleased. His mother, on seeing the return of her prodigal son, wept openly with joy. Together they entered the house and drank tea whilst Tubs explained in detail how he could not have let them know of his arrival in the UK. His father, ex-RN and proud of his days in the Senior Service, could not grasp the situation, but still managed to look pleased at his home-coming.

Tubs felt disorientated, and hardly able to communicate after his long journey. He was now acclimatised to living in Nairobi at an altitude in excess of five thousand feet, and having flown over three thousand miles, the change in tem-perature and altitude was making his teeth chatter. Still his father questioned him on how he was to return to Nairobi, failing the availability of an 'indulgence flight'. The plan, foolproof according to Dickie, was to return on the Beverley flight from Abingdon in three days time. Finally, his father looked satisfied saying, 'OK, let's go to bed.'

Tubs stumbled upstairs with his bag. God, he was tired. He tore off his clothing, fearful that he might drop exhausted onto the floor. Immediately his head hit the pillow, he was gone into a state of oblivion…

16. *The Return Trip*

After what seemed a very short sleep he was awakened by his father pulling open the bedroom curtains to expose the stark grey light and cold air.

'It's not a bad day,' said his father, peering into the rain and murk. 'It might clear up later.'

Lifting himself wearily from the bed Tubs knew he could expect no sympathy from his father who, having never flown, could not understand the disorientation he felt. Still, he looked forward to the opportunity of drinking some good Northern beer and with any luck renewing some old acquaintances. Downstairs his mother was lovingly cooking him a full English fried breakfast, which he ate with relish.

His father had decided to take some time off from his beloved Lead Works and was busy polishing his shoes in the kitchen. The weather had improved, by way of it ceasing to rain, and Tubs was keen to leave the house and attempt to locate some of his old friends in the many pubs of Chester. Kissing his mother, who was still marvelling at the cigarette lighter he had bought whilst inebriated in Malta, Tubs walked off down the road, wearing his thickest sweater and overcoat to ward off the biting cold. Over the canal bridge he spied the overalled figure of his old school-friend Stuart Begby, on the forecourt of his father's garage business.

'Look what the cat's brought in!' shouted Begby.

They shook hands warmly. They had been good friends and Tubs had taken more than a passing fancy to his older sister. Time was short, Stuart had a clutch to fit, so Tubs arranged to meet later in the Pied Bull and made his way to the town centre, keen to make the most of his short break.

Finding himself at City Road he could not resist a drink in the Central Bars. He pushed his way through the revolving door, slumped onto one of the many vacant chromium-plated stools and ordered a pint of draught Bass. The bar was empty excepting for the barmaid, who sported a bad case of acne, was short and thin, and failed to excite him in any way. Perhaps it was the cold weather, he pondered. He had no female contacts left in Chester, having received a 'Dear John' letter some time ago from his last female acquaintance – a market gardener's daughter who had decided to take her produce elsewhere. He smiled as he remembered pinning it to the NAAFI 'Dear John' noticeboard back in Nairobi.

He gazed out of the window as steady rain began to fall and then, pulling up his overcoat collar, sauntered out and headed for 'Blossoms Bar'. Harry, the barman was pleased to see him and even bought him a drink, a rare occasion for Harry. They had a few more drinks, the time passing pleas-antly enough, and with a cheery 'Look after yourself mate,' Tubs departed.

He felt as if in a time capsule. Wherever he went the peo-ple he enquired after had either changed jobs, left the area, emigrated, or were on holiday. Having promised to return for lunch he called into a nearby off-licence to buy a few bottles of his mother's favourite tipple, Mackeson. He clambered aboard the heavily-laden bus home with a carrier bag full of clinking Mackeson bottles, his coat clingingly damp and cold. He called in at The Bridge Inn, where he sank two double whiskies but still arrived in plenty of time for lunch. As he walked through the door his mother excitedly said, 'A friend of yours called Dickie has just been on the phone. Said it was urgent.'

'Great,' thought Tubs, 'I wonder what he's been up to? Probably wants bailing out from the nick.'

Without further ado he phoned the number Dickie had left.

'How're you doing, you old bastard?' he began cheerfully.

Dickie's reply was uncharacteristically serious.

'We've been offloaded for the Beverley flight on the way back.'

Tubs almost dropped the phone in disbelief.

'Christ,' he thought, 'I'm stuck here without a flight back and no money!'

'But it's not the end of the world,' Dickie continued, 'there's another Beverly flight, but you'll have to be packed and ready to go, day or night.'

'I don't care. Just get me back without having to go to the bank for a loan,' said Tubs.

'You can rely on me,' Dickie assured him, 'Ring me to-morrow at noon. I'm just going out to get pissed.'

The phone went dead. Tubs was in a trance. He dare not show his parents he was concerned, they would immediately want to know why. Against his better judgement, he put his faith in Dickie and silently prayed for success.

His mother asked him to telephone his brother Reg and this he did as she asked; he was determined to make his short visit a pleasure for his mother. Neighbours appeared and invited him round for a drink. Suddenly feeling wanted, he began to feel happier still as he consumed an assortment of spirits at each house he visited. Thinking ahead, he decided to stay at home that night, with Dickie's words 'be packed and ready to go anytime, night or day' ringing in his ears. Urged on by his mother he partook liberally of his father's Christmas stock of booze. She prepared a huge meal and the evening was spent sifting through the many photographs Tubs had sent home. Brimful of alcohol he excused himself at 2200 hours and retired to bed.

Next morning, almost secretly, he packed what little clothes he had. At 10 o'clock he walked quietly the route he had made a thousand times before to the pub across the canal bridge. It was not a pub known for its cleanliness, and at this time only a few of the veteran brigade propped up the beer-stained bar. He drank eagerly, his mind very much on Dickie's midday call. At 11.30 he left and swiftly walked the path home, to find his mother had already poured him a large whisky 'to keep out the cold'. At 12.10 the telephone rang and almost in a trance with apprehensive he picked up the receiver to hear Dickie's voice.

'The good news is that we are on a Beverley flight from Abingdon. The bad news is that it's leaving at 0615 tomorrow.'

Tubs was elated but slightly shaken. 'Christ,' he said, 'how the hell do I get to Abingdon in that time?'

'There are plenty of trains to Oxford,' said Dickie reassuringly.

'Where do we meet?'

'Ask for the transit billet and tell them that Air Movements have booked you on the 0615 flight to Eastleigh. Bye...'

Pouring himself another whisky Tubs explained to his mother that he had to leave, trying hard to ease the blow of his departure and promising to write weekly. His father arrived, and not realising the amount of alcohol Tubs had already consumed, quickly opened another bottle, plying his wife with sherry in the hope of stabilising her emotions. Tubs checked the train timetable and, as usual, Dickie was right. The train would arrive at 3am. He made a few quick phone calls, apologising to the friends he had promised to meet that night.

His mother, looking sad, but having accepted the situation, was dutifully making sandwiches in the kitchen. Father, trying hard to keep a party mood, refilled glasses enthusiastically, keen to make Tubs' imminent departure as unemotional as possible. Tubs did not usually relate to his father's strict views on life, but the hours drifted by cordially enough, fuelled by an abundance of northern food, whisky and cigars. Soon it was time to leave for the darkness of

Chester General railway station, the scene of many tearful departures in the past. His father proudly drove the leather-seated Rover 14, its bodywork gleaming.

Alongside the Oxford train, Tubs pumped his father's hand cheerfully. His mother, love shining in her eyes, held his hand as the guard began to close the carriage doors. Then, with a wave and a promise to 'see you again in a few months' Tubs began his journey back to Eastleigh.

On reflection his visit to the UK had been a mixture of success and failure. He had succeeded in brightening his mother's life, and to a certain degree his father's, but he had failed miserably in relocating to his friends in the UK and had been reminded of the cold, wet and dull quality of life of postwar Britain. Tiredness and cold wafted over him in the unheated carriage until he drifted off into a dream of Kenya, the country he was learning to love like a mistress – one to whom he could not wait to return.

With a bang the train hit the buffers at Oxford and Tubs awoke with a start. It was 3am and his body was stiff with cold. Leaving the station he peered for the gloom for a telephone, and on finding one, found a TA corporal already using it. On leaving the booth the TA man said, 'I've just arranged a lift to RAF Abingdon, so if that's what you're looking for, the truck will be here in ten minutes.'

'Thanks,' said Tubs, eying the corporal's huge kitbag.

'Doing a parachute jump at 0800 but feel too fucked to walk, never mind jump,' said the corporal, laughingly.

He seemed nice enough, but Tubs could never understand why anyone would voluntarily jump out of an aircraft unless it was about to crash. Within minutes the truck arrived and they climbed in, Tubs helping the corporal with his huge kitbag. Arriving at Abingdon he reported to the Guardroom.

'Name's SAC Ryan, flying out on the 0615 flight to Eastleigh; can you steer me to the transit billet?' he asked the Duty Sergeant, whose Alsatian guard dog eyed him suspiciously from under a table.

'Follow me my lad,' he said, walking out into the approaching dawn and light rain. It was a short walk and soon the sergeant opened the battered wooden door with its badly painted sign 'Transit Only'. Looking into the billet he said, 'That bastard over there is dead lucky not to be in the cells; he arrived pissed at 0100 and fell down at the gate, so we had to carry him in here.'

After thanking the retreating sergeant Tubs looked down at the sleeping silhouette. There was no mistaking it. It was Dickie. Tubs lay on his bed but there was no point in going to sleep. His luminous watch, glowing in the dark, registered 0400, and the light of dawn was already evident through the grime of the windows.

As their departure time approached Dickie arose and began shuffling around his bed, collecting his belongings. They crept out of the billet in silence, for fear of waking the other inmates. They had always eaten heartily before flying and especially after a hard night, and today was no exception. They wolfed down a buffet-style English breakfast, washed down with plenty of strong tea. The sky was grey and light rain was falling as they checked into Air Movements with their minimum of baggage, and soon they were boarding the Beverley, climbing the steep steps to the passenger area, as they had done so many times before.

The crew carried out their pre-flight checks and the aircraft, heaving under its load, trundled out onto the runway. Power on, flaps down and into the wind, the Beverley lumbered into the sky, heading south towards Malta. Levelling off at nine thousand feet, the aircraft being unpressurised, oxygen bottles were opened in case of emergency.

The Beverley, heavily laden with the Canberra fuselage below them, whilst the fitting crew slept huddled on the passenger deck, began to eat up the air miles as if keen to reach Malta. The sun came up, forcing the passengers to shield their eyes, and soon the Island of Gozo appeared under the huge wing and the aircraft began its descent to land at Luqa. Formality was cut to zero, the refuelling stop taking barely forty minutes, and soon they were in the air again, heading for El Adem and a welcome night-stop. The drone of the aircraft lulled them again to sleep until a warning message over the intercom of 'seat-belts – could be rough – landing in ten minutes' from the pilot, shattered their dreams.

The aircraft descended, hit the runway and bounced fifty feet into the air. With power off it dropped alarmingly to bounce again, brakes screaming, finally landing at the end of the runway, a few hundred yards from the wire fence.

'Fucking hell! No wonder he wanted us to put seat belts on. Just to make sure we not asleep when we died!' laughed Dickie, even he a little shocked at the bumpy landing.

The Loadmaster appeared at the doorway, cheerful as ever.

'See you at 1030 tomorrow chaps,' he shouted.

Tubs and Dickie already had their game plan for this night-stop: a good session in the mess, an early morning call, and then a lift to Tobruk, some eighteen miles down the road, to take some pictures.

They were billeted in tents and the desert wind was already forcing sand through the tent flap and into their sleeping bags. They cared not, for this was just another venture, another day. The mess bar only sold spirits, as beer could not transported this far or stored in this heat. They quickly found a friendly LAC from MT and badgered him for a ride into Tobruk, and after half a bottle of vodka he agreed to pick them up at 0630 drive them to the town, wait half an hour, and then drive them back.

Tubs did not remember going to bed, just being steered between two shoulders and laid onto his sleeping bag. However, he did feel the cold desert wind and was aware of eating sand as it was driven under the tent flap. At 0600 the LAC from MT arrived and peered with disbelief at Tubs prostrate body covered with sand.

They boarded the Land Rover and sped off towards Tobruk, on the way witnessing the spectacle of hundreds of German and British World War Two tanks still quietly rusting in the desert, never to fight again. The LAC obligingly took a photograph of them alongside a German tank.

At Tobruk, eager to rid themselves of the sand clinging to their bodies, they donned swimming trunks and dived into the clear blue sea. Time went quickly, and soon they were back at Air Movements and the awaiting aircraft.

Formalities completed the Beverley, with No.47 squadron proudly painted on the tail fin, took off and headed for Khartoum. The flight became increasingly rough and with a powerful headwind and a full load, the aircraft was forced down to 150 knots, making it vulnerable to the whims of vertical currents. Its airframe creaked as it fought its way to cruising altitude, and the fitting crew queued to empty their stomachs in the chemical toilet. The Loadmaster appeared, to ensure all baggage was correctly stowed, and even he looked far from happy with the conditions. Flashes of light lit the fuselage as the aircraft hit an electrical storm, and the occupants held onto their seats. All conversation was now drowned by the noise of the engines as the captain searched for a way around the storm.

At length the Loadmaster appeared again, his worried look now replaced with his usual smile.

'We're stopping at Khartoum for breakfast,' he shouted. 'Used a lot of fuel due to the storm.'

The Beverley's engine note decreased, as if with relief, and the nose dropped in preparation for the landing at Khartoum. The big transport aircraft bumped, rolled, and with a cheer from the Canberra fitting crew, finally landed at Khartoum.

Walking the short distance to the airport lounge, they found plates of scrambled eggs and toast awaiting them. They ate heartily, Tubs and Dickie already thinking ahead to their next stop, RAF Eastleigh. After their delicious breakfast they reflected that this could well be their last in Khartoum, as neither of them could envisage that they would ever pass this way again. The Canberra fitters looked ashen as they made their way to the airport toilet to reload with airsickness pills.

After a short while they took off again, flying directly into the sun, the Beverley's engines cruising happily, as if knowing this was the last leg of the journey. At last, and with a cheer as the loadmaster noted the marker some thirty miles from Eastleigh, the aircraft began its descent. Slowly, as if the captain was keen to make the perfect landing, he steered the huge transport onto the murram runway and instant applying reverse pitch, smoothly kissed the ground to land.

It had been an eventful round trip of ten thousand miles in nine days. They climbed out of the aircraft, clutching their luggage, Dickie thanking the aircrew in his usual manner. The weather was glorious and the time was 1615. They agreed, laughingly, that if this was the RAF they liked it, and if this was Kenya then they liked it even better!

17. More Fun in Mombasa

Back at Eastleigh Dickie, being his usual thoughtful self, distributed bottles of brown ale he had purchased just prior to departure from Stanstead. In return, they were invited down to the NAAFI for a 'coming home party', which ended, as usual, in slurred speech for all concerned as they staggered home to their pits.

Next day Tubs saw Dickie marching briskly past the Orderly Room, his arms full of maps.

'Guess what?' he shouted. 'Saw the SATCO today and he wanted to know why we came back from the UK so early. Seems he sent a signal for us to be placed on the incoming Britannia detachment's manifest as supernumerary crew.'

'Bollocks!' Tubs shouted back.

The SATCO was prone to do kind deeds at the most unusual times, and it was ironic that they had both endured the knife-edge decision of what flight to take to avoid the embarrassment of having to pay the airline fare in order to return to Eastleigh before their leave expired.

Before Tubs could comment further, Dickie had disappeared. He wrote home, leading off with, 'Well, how are you in that wet and miserable land?' The weather during their trip home had been diabolical and had been described by Dickie as 'officially fucking awful'. In contrast, the weather in Nairobi was glorious and with little to do Tubs main task was to rally the dhobi boy to make more 'chai'.

He had been rejuvenated by his trip home, and by receiving a letter from his army friend Dave Atkins, who was now demobbed and had returned to his civilian job in the town hall as a clerk. Tubs swore not to do the same. He sent home a large Christmas card with a long letter to appease his mother.

The whole of the billet shared the Christmas cake his mother had lovingly sent him. They were a happy bunch. If someone didn't have enough money to visit the station cinema someone else would lend the money or, more often than not, pay, the favour being returned at a later date. If you had no money for a drink, someone would buy you one. Morale was good; there was a feeling of camaraderie within the RAF which did not exist in civilian life.

Christmas stand-down was to be from 23rd to 27th December, plus New Year's Day off, for the benefit of the many Scotsmen on the station.

Dead on 0800 Flight Lieutenant McEwan breezed into the Orderly Room.

'Fancy doing me a favour and typing this for me?' he queried, pushing a bundle of badly-written notes headed 'Tennis Club Annual General Meeting' before Tubs' eyes. He had never seen the tall Flight Lieutenant before, but had little to do and was eager to please.

'No problem Sir. It'll be done within the hour.'

The Flight Lieutenant left, whistling into the distance. Dead on the hour he reappeared, like the proverbial cuckoo in a clock, to collect his typing.

'OK Sir?' queried Tubs.

'Nicely,' was the reply. 'Look… I'm with the Varsity detachment and we're flying down to Mombasa tomorrow, and we've got two spare seats if you want a ride.'

Tubs was delighted and keen to tell Dickie, for this would be the first 'jolly' that Dickie's silver tongue had not delivered. Quickly he rang him on the Wing Commander's internal phone.

'We've got a lift to Mombasa tomorrow with the Varsity detatchment,' he almost shouted.

'Bloody hell, you'll honk your ring up in that old sickbag!' came Dickie's quick reply.

Tubs began to plan ahead for his trip, excited at the thought of seeing Layla again. At 0700 they reported to 70 Squadron Ops for the Varsity flight and, dead on time, at 0730 they boarded the Varsity, known affectionately as 'the flying pig' by the aircrew and 'sick-bag' by its passengers. They took off, and were soon buffeted by early morning currents across the desert, the two-engine transport bucking like a wild horse as it strained to reach cruising altitude over the snow-capped peak of Mount Kilimanjaro.

Soon they began the long approach into Mombasa airport, the captain making two 'passes' to enable both pilots to experience the landing technique, before touching down at the far end of the field, ready for refuelling.

The captain appeared from the cockpit, sweat pouring from his brow, as the early morning sun rose into the sky.

'Hope you had a nice flight. A little rough I'm afraid. Take-off is at 1900 hours, so be here by 1830 latest.'

He disappeared back into the cockpit.

Tubs and Dickie hurried from the airport and hailed a taxi into town. Soon they were driving along the wide streets with its huge palm trees standing like sentries either side of the road and into Kilindini Road, with its world famous elephant tusks spanning the road and its many mosques.

'New Bristol upset sana Raffiki,' shouted Dickie to the driver, above the noise and rattle of the vehicle's ancient engine. Soon they were at the door of the New Bristol, laughingly called a hotel, with Dickie paying off the taxi driver with a cheery 'Kwaheri Raffiki.'

They made their way into the empty bar and ordered two large Tuskers to stave off the dehydration of the flight and to wash the dust from their mouths. Tubs was eager to find Layla and walked out to the back room of the bar, where the kitchen was situated, to find her taking glasses out of an antiquated dishwasher and polishing them lovingly to gleam like pearls in the light. She wore an old-fashioned butcher's apron over a short blue skirt and blouse which matched her high-heeled blue shoes.

He stood gazing at her, enchanted, until he could wait no longer, and then ran to her, lifting her high into the air, whispering 'Layla darling,' into her ear. She smelt of perfumed soap and her eyes sparkled and radiated happiness as she looked into his eyes. They held each other in a long embrace until Dickie appeared at the door, badly impersonating a policeman by bending his legs and rolling his eyes whilst repeating, 'Hello, hello, hello, what's going on here then?

'If you want Rita, she'll be back in ten minutes,' said Layla, pre-empting Dickie's next sentence, at which point he discreetly returned to the bar and his awaiting drink.

'How have you been, darling?' said Layla, holding Tubs' hand, her face still flushed with excitement.

'Never been better,' said Tubs, grasping her around her slim waist and kissing her passionately to reinforce his words. He looked at her again. She was half-French; her father had disappeared mysteriously, leaving Layla and her mother to fend for themselves, but with enough money to ensure that they lived slightly above the normal local lifestyle. In the front bar they could hear that Rita had returned and Dickie was entertaining her with some risqué RAF jokes.

Layla arranged to take the rest of the day off and after a short discussion the four of them set of for Fort Jesus for lunch and sightseeing. Layla was happy but puzzled. She knew that she was on the brink of falling in love with this overweight airman, but her mother had warned her before about the antics and conduct she could expect from Europeans looking for little more than a 'good time' before returning to the UK. Could Tubs fit into this category? She decided not. The meal at the steak bar was a success and having consumed two bottles of wine and a handful of beers they were 'at ease' with each other, and eager to make the most of the day.

Tubs had noticed for some time Layla looking enviously at African bead bracelets, and taking her hand led her into a jewellers, where he bought her choice and was quickly rewarded with an impromptu kiss. Dickie was across the street, haggling with an African market-trader to buy Rita a white handbag. The four looped arms and walked four abreast along the wide pavements of downtown Mombasa. It became increasingly hot, the heat-haze rising in the distance, and Layla suggested a drink at her mother's house, situated on the road leading to the airport.

After hailing a taxi, they had travelled but a short distance when they arrived at Layla's home, a large, flat-roofed concrete house, painted a fetching biscuit colour, surrounded by a bright yellow fence. The garden, front and rear, was bedecked with flowers, displaying a mass of colour. The front door was carved in Arab style and varnished to a high gloss. Inside the tiled floor was covered with oval-shaped African mats and the walls held an assortment of modern prints. It was neat, clean and very tidy.

'Have a whisky,' said Layla, pouring a large measure into a highball glass and smiling at Tubs' eager response. 'I'll show you around.' Taking his hand she led him to her room, the smell of jasmine filling his nostrils as he neared it. The room was decorated stark white, with a large ceiling fan gently rotating. He turned towards her as if in a trance and, emboldened by the whisky, slowly undid the buttons on her blouse until she stood exposed to the waist, smiling into his eyes, as if anticipating the outcome of this foreplay. Now it was her turn to remove his sweat-stained cotton shirt and lovingly kiss his chest, which developed into a passionate embrace that made them both gasp with pleasure.

'You like?' she queried.

He nodded, as if in a dream, looking down at her beautiful sand-coloured body as he undid the buttons on her short skirt, his hands trembling with desire. Naked, bar a minuscule pair of panties and her high-heeled shoes, she lay down on the bed, beckoning him to join her. He threw his shoes noisily into a corner of the room and lay down beside her, their hands eager to explore each other's bodies, the only noise being the whirring of the ceiling fan.

Slowly, he eased off her panties and entered her, watching fascinated as her face contorted with ecstasy. They writhed together, drunk with passion, until they reached orgasm simultaneously, like two thoroughbred horses dead-heating in a race. Their breathing finally abated to its normal pace and they lovingly, longingly hugged and kissed each other from head to toe. He kissed her mouth – God, how he loved her mouth – rich, ruby-red and pouting.

They dressed, and returned to the lounge to find Rita and Dickie staring longingly at each other, with Rita's crumpled skirt showing proof of recent sexual activity. Tubs and Layla were in a world of their own, tired but happy after their lovemaking.

But soon it was time to leave for the airport and they bundled into a nearby taxi. It was the first time that Layla had bothered to see him off at the airport but on arrival there was little time for anything more than a quick drink, each couple holding hands, with Tubs promising to write to Layla on his return to Eastleigh. The aircrew beckoned them forward and Tubs kissed Layla passionately on the lips, taking one last look at her lovely legs as he made his way to the aircraft.

The girls waved as the aircraft began to taxi out and the Loadmaster appeared. Spying Tubs he queried playfully,

'Is that your girlfriend?'

Tubs nodded.

'Very, very nice,' said the loadmaster, reverently, clicking his teeth as he disappeared into the loading bay.

As the Varsity gathered speed they waved out of the window to the girls until the aircraft climbed away on its return journey to Eastleigh.

The two hundred miles were spanned without incident and on landing Tubs looked across to Dickie as he unfastened his seat belt.

'Had a good day?' he asked.

'Sure have – and a hard one,' replied Dickie, with a satisfied grin.

18.   *Out of Bounds*

Life at Eastleigh now quietened down in anticipation of the alcoholic furore promised by the Christmas break – to which the NAAFI management had pledged to contribute by charging only one East African shilling for a beer or a shot of spirits.

Tubs had nothing much to do but watch the Beverleys roar off into the pale blue sky and write long, tedious letters home, describing the daily events. He wrote to Layla, enclosing a large Christmas card and a silk scarf, bought after much thought, from the New Stanley Hotel's gift shop. There was no doubt in his mind that she would be pleased with her present.

On December 23rd all hell broke loose, at least, according to the MPs, as every section of the camp held its own version of a Christmas party. Flying Wing HQ was no exception. Dickie, red-faced but still coherent, arrived at the door of the Orderly Room at mid-day as the Group Captain and a Corporal, both the worse for wear and thinking little of the consequences in the New Year, began to lead the others in singing a bawdy version of 'Noel, Noel'.

Group Captain Joel was known as a hard but fair man and was well liked by all ranks. Short and stocky, he was an ex-fighter pilot and known by other pilots as the only man to have landed a Beverley at Eastleigh after bouncing the aircraft three times. He looked immaculate, his uniform at its best, and was soon leading the 'No-el, No-el', chorus. The air was filled with happiness and a generous collection had been made for the ebullient African boy, Christopher, who looked on, bemused, drinking his English beer and marvelling at the antics of the party. Forever smiling and eager to please, he had amassed a huge wardrobe of European clothes, left by servicemen heading for the UK and demob.

The festivities continued throughout the day until Tubs and Dickie decided it would be wiser to return to West Site while they could still stand. They walked the perimeter track and joined No.70 Squadron's festivities with their many friends in the Beverley crew room. They drank eagerly and laughingly until it was time to make their way home, the wooden veranda resounding under their feet, and on reaching the billet they quickly undressed, climbed under their mosquito nets and into their beds.

Christmas was almost at hand. The year was 1961 and outside the Kenyan moon shone down on them as they slept. On Christmas day the time-honoured practice of officers serving the men was carried out in the Mess, and with the catering staff at their very best it was Dickie who led 'three cheers for the catering staff', a glass of Tusker in his hand.

The afternoon was spent lounging in the sun alongside an army of empty beer bottles. It was a peaceful day. No flying, no worries, just time to take a long look at life as it should be, hedonistic, free, and enjoyed to the full.

Christmas came and went and although the Mau Mau had long been disbanded there were still disturbing accounts of families attached with pangas, usually told in gory detail by some drunken Kenyan in the Norfolk Hotel late on Saturday afternoons. There was no doubt that the atrocities by the Mau Mau were true in many cases. The testimony of those who witnessed pregnant Masai women being cut open and their babies crudely sewn to their tongues were too many to be other than fact. In the bars of Nairobi it was now fashionable for suited and educated Africans to talk about the 'ending of the colonial government' and both Tubs and Dickie realised that this would not take long to achieve.

'We're in their lovely country and one day they'll tell us to leave, so let's be friendly and helpful,' said Tubs gesticulating with his arms.

'You're damn right! I'm not here to throw my weight around,' replied Dickie.

In the following weeks Dickie struck up a friendship with an LAC called Kelly and they had taken to driving in Kelly's battered Ford to a bar frequented by leading Kenyan politician Tom Mboya. In the back bar they had both listened entranced to his sincere philosophy that when the colonial government had left Kenya for good he would make a land where black and white would live together in peaceful harmony, and most importantly, mutual respect. Dickie would speak at length with Tom Mboia and his followers, sipping beer, and was quickly accepted, because although white and in the RAF as a conscript, he had a sympathetic ear. It was after such a session that all three set off, fired with alcohol, in Kelly's dusty and rattling Ford to a bar recommended by one of Tom Mboia's henchmen. Speaking Swahili with ease, Kelly, short and wearing a pair of glasses that might have accounted for his erratic driving, ordered a tray of beers, which quickly arrived.

Everyone in the bar was African and all seemed friendly, if a little surprised to see white company in this part of town. They sat and listened as Kelly preached his communistic view of what should happen to Kenya, and before long the audience had grown to everyone in the bar, who listened as if mesmerised by Kelly's forecast of a glowing future after the white administration had served its end. Kelly seemed bent on talking directly to a tall Afro/Indian girl in the group, whose eyes rolled with delight as she noticed his interest. Looking out of the front of the bar Tubs noticed the absence of streetlights and wondered how far from the main area of Nairobi they had strayed. Kelly droned on, becoming more political and more inebriated by the minute. Pointing to his watch Tubs caught Kelly's eye and he finally waved his arms resignedly saying, 'Sorry raffikis, we'll have to go.'

By this time the girl had moved alongside Kelly and was holding his arm.

'We'll drop her off,' said Kelly,' his speech slurred.

They set off, and within minutes stopped outside a very small house with a sheet metal roof. The girl began to pull Kelly out of the car, motioning to the house, and at first he appeared to be refusing her offer. But it soon became evident that he had succumbed to her attentions and they entered the house hand in hand.

Tubs looked down the road. There were no lights and spotting a scraggy mongrel dog he walked over to it and began to scratch the its head as a sign of affection.

He looked back to see Kelly and the girl getting into the back of an ancient Ford which was parked outside the house. They disappeared except for a brief glimpse of flailing arms, followed by the up and down movement of the rear suspension, synchronised with the creaking of the chassis as it complained of the sexual activity within. The dog looked up into Tubs' face knowingly as they sat on the murram road, listening to the gradually increasing tempo of the creaking and the occasional groans emanating from its open windows.

At length the movement ceased and the girl ran into the house, adjusting her dress as she went. Kelly reappeared, his sweat-stained face and crumpled clothes a testament to his recent activities.

'Sorry about that, the bitch couldn't resist me,' he said arrogantly. Tubs laughed within. They sped off, with Kelly driving like the wind until a pair of strong headlights appeared in their path.

'Fucking hell, it's the MPs,' said Kelly, stopping, and suddenly realising that another Land Rover had pulled up behind. In the headlights strode an MP, a Flight Sergeant no less, complete with a lean and hungry-looking Alsatian.

'It's OK, it's Flt Sgt Mullins. I play rugby for his team,' said Kelly, laughing out loud in relief.

The Flight Sergeant reached the window.

'Give me your ID airman,' he demanded.

Kelly laughed again.

'It's me Flight Sergeant, your wing-half,' he said.

'LAC Kelly, you are under arrest for being out of bounds and so is your passenger. Give me your IDs now!' he barked.

Kelly flung his ID at the Flight Sergeant, shouting at the top of his voice so that most of the Nairobi suburban area could hear him. 'You fat bastard, the next time we play I'll rip your head off!' He was shaking with rage, sweat dripping from his face.

Tubs tried hard to pacify him and to apologise for his outburst but the Flight Sergeant was not impressed.

With Kelly once again in the driving seat they drove back to Eastleigh, escorted front and rear by the MPs. To Kelly's indignation added to his charge was 'consorting with a known prostitute' – a piece of information apparently supplied by the Kenyan Civil Police.

Tomorrow, in the cold light of day, Tubs would have the dubious pleasure of adding himself to the long list of those charged 'OOB' and wondered how many days he would be forced to serve in the guardroom.

At 0800 next day Tubs arrived to unlock the Orderly Room to find the ominous-looking Charge Form RAF 252 pushed under the door. Tearing open the envelope he was pleased to find his charge simply read, 'LAC Ryan found out of bounds'. The following two foolscap sheets dealt in detail with Kelly's remarks upon his arrest and did not augur well for his chances of being let off lightly.

Tubs quickly typed out the charges and placed them on the Adjutant's desk. To his delight he found out that Flight Lieutenant Binedell was off sick and his Deputy, a junior Flight Lieutenant from Air Traffic, would hear the charge.

At 10.00 the SWO marched him in and he stood before the Deputy Adjutant, trying to look remorseful.

'How do you plead to this charge?' asked the young Flight Lieutenant, his face looking down onto the shining desktop.

'No excuses, guilty,' replied Tubs.

'Do not make a habit of this. You are confined to camp for three days,' said the kind-hearted Flight Lieutenant.

Next up was Kelly, who stood there, mindful of the remarks he had made whilst drunk, to a SNCO, and fully fearing the worst.

'How do you plead to these charges?' queried the Flight Lieutenant, blandly, as if reading the procedure direct from QRs.

'Guilty and very sorry,' said Kelly.

'You were found out of bounds with a known prostitute,' counted the Flight Lieutenant.

'I did not know this and would certainly not have given her a lift if I had Sir,' replied Kelly, now warming to the verbal war.

'Were you drunk?'

'No, but I had downed a few beers,' was the quick reply.

'You made threatening remarks to the SNCO here in the course of his duty. In view of that fact, is there any reason why this matter should not be referred to a court martial?'

'Sir, anything I said was on the spur of the moment and is out of character as I was very annoyed with myself for being found in such an embarrassing situation,' said Kelly, staring at his shoes.

The Flight Lieutenant turned to the SNCO and asked pointedly, 'Well, Flight, its down to you. If you want to remove some of the charges we'll dispense with the Group Captain and the court martial and issue punishment here and now.'

The Flight Sergeant stepped forward.

'In view of the apology and the fact that it was a drunken escapade, I'm prepared to leave the charge as Ryan's.'

'Kelly,' said the Flight Lieutenant, you're bloody lucky. Five days in the guardroom for you, and if you come back again God help you.'

Kelly turned and marched briskly out.

19. A Family Visit

The days went seemingly endlessly on and Tubs noticed, to his amazement, his name on Station Standing Orders, designating him to Station Duties Roster. Every member at Eastleigh had to undergo five days of armed duties, which comprised twelve hours each day at Embakasi airport and on school bus escorts and fire pickets. Though tough sleep-wise, most airmen thought of it as a refreshing change from their normal duties. No one enjoyed it more than Tubs, who enjoyed his armed guard stint at Embakasi, giving him a chance to smile at the incoming air hostesses whilst guarding the Hunter aircraft of 208 Squadron.

During the week he received a letter from his parents telling him of their forthcoming holiday in Bournemouth. The South Coast of England seemed a long way away, and Bournemouth a very distant memory. With seven months still to serve in the RAF he was enjoying life so much that he could not, nor would not, visualise life back in the UK.

Back in Kenya the news from the Northern Frontier District was bad. Many of the tribes were endangered by famine and local Africans prayed daily for their fellow tribesmen in their hour of need. The African elections were under way and despite a bit of shouting and waving at the rallies up and down the country there was little trouble.

Prior to Christmas, Tubs had been talking to Wing Commander Taylor in the company of Christopher, their ever-smiling African tea-boy. The Wing Commander, decked out in his No.1 uniform as if still at Cranwell, had inquired of Christopher, 'Where do you come from?'

'My family is at Kisumu,' replied Christopher, continuing to sweep the floor conscientiously.

'Ryan, next time there is a Twin Pioneer flight to Kisumu let me know and we'll fly young Christopher home for the day,' said the Winco, before disappearing into his office.

Peering at the Ops Room log next day Tubs spotted a flight to Gil Gil, Nakuru and on to Kisumu, returning the same day. Hot-foot he returned to the Wing Commander's office to find he had gone home and was not available until next day. Finding Christopher he telephoned the Winco at home, reminding him of his promise to the now highly-excited Christopher.

'OK, Ryan, I'll try and get hold of the OC No.21 Squadron tonight, but go down to the squadron in the morning at 0630 with Christopher and tell them it's been cleared by me. You'd better go as escort, and be sure to have a nice day.'

'Many thanks Sir,' replied Tubs, truly grateful for the day off.

Christopher was delighted and hurried home excitedly to tell his wife, having been briefed to be at 21 Squadron Ops at 0615.

Tubs, dressed in his newly-starched KD long trousers and shirt, arrived next day as the Kenyan dawn began to shine on the hangar door of No.21 Squadron, the bright orange sun rising slowly into the sky as if on a string. There were no

personnel around except a lonely SAC looking over the Twin
Pioneer which stood on the perimeter track, fuelled-up and
ready for the Kisumu flight.

At 0630 the aircrew arrived in a Land Rover and, walking
up the perimeter track could be seen Christopher, wearing a
European suit, black shoes, a loud tie and looking very happy.
Tubs took Christopher into the Operations Room and finding Flight Lieutenant Young donning his flying suit quickly
saluted and said, 'I believe we're flying down to Kisumu with
you Sir?'

'Really, who said so?' was the sarcastic reply.

Tubs was a little taken aback but countered, 'Wing Commander Taylor was going to speak to the OC 21 Squadron
last night to arrange it Sir.'

'Just you?' queried the pilot.

'No, myself and Christopher,' said Tubs, pointing to the
smiling African.

'I don't fly bloody Africans,' said the pilot, but you can
gladly come.'

'Christ,' thought Tubs, 'just what I need – a racist pilot
with a hangover.' Perhaps he had not explained the position
clearly.

'Wing Commander Taylor said Christopher could fly
down to see his family for the day and I'm sorry if you did
not get the message,' said Tubs apologetically.

Flight Lieutenant Young did not want to fly the African
and his face showed it, but neither did he want a confronta-
tion with the Wing Commander. He was quiet for a moment

until he had finally tied the laces of his flying boots and then he played his ace card.

'Where's the blood chit for the African?' he asked.

Tubs froze. No-one had remembered that Christopher, being a civilian, would need an indemnity form in case of an accident.

'I'll go and get one and get it signed,' said Tubs, running from the room and jumping on the Section bike. He pedalled as if his life depended on it towards the Orderly Room, and as he looked back he could see the ground crew were placing the aircraft in position. Throwing the bike against the Orderly Room wall he unlocked the office and rummaged in the Adjutant's drawer before finding the precious 'blood chit'. He cursed the pilot and also himself for not remembering that the documentation was necessary to fly a civilian. He pedalled back across the perimeter track, his legs aching with the effort and arrived at the Ops Room to find the navigator making his way to the aircraft. Grabbing Christopher by the arm, he made him quickly sign the form, the benevolent African still oblivious to the hostile demeanour of the pilot.

Tubs approached Flight Lieutenant Young, saluting him with great gusto. 'Here's the blood chit duly signed, Sir.'

'What's your name?' asked the pilot, his face white with rage.

'Ryan Sir,' replied Tubs.

The pilot continued his tirade.

'OK Ryan. I have the blood-chit. You and you alone are in complete charge of the African. If he's sick in flight you clean it up. If he's lost in Kisumu you bloody stay there and find him. Do we understand each other?'

'Perfectly Sir,' replied Tubs, thinking inwardly 'what a bloody bastard'.

The three of them walked over to the aircraft, Tubs and Christopher climbing in at the rear door. He fastened Christopher's seat belt and instructed him what to do in case of an emergency. The Twin Pioneer trundled out, turned into wind, and within seconds they were airborne and on the way to Gil Gil. With the pilot's words still ringing in his ears, 'If he's sick you clean it up,' Tubs set about showing Christopher where the small chemical toilet was situated.

Christopher showed no fear whatsoever of the flight and was ceaselessly asking Tubs where they were. The thought of seeing his family again in Kisumu showed by way of an ever-present smile of happiness radiating from his face. They landed at Gil Gil and a couple of heavy crates of medical syringes were stacked at the rear before the quick turnaround and take-off.

The navigator appeared, smiling, and apologised for the pilot's lack of humour before they left.

'Fact is, Ryan, we should have been told last night due to the weight restriction.' He left shaking his head, adding, 'And it's going to get bloody rough according to the Met report.'

Christopher sat, fascinated, as the aircraft descended into Nakuru. Under the port wing could be seen the spectacle of the million flamingos who resided on the lake.

After landing, even more freight was stacked high at the rear door and Tubs realised that it could well have been concern over their laden weight that had made the pilot so 'touchy' before they left rather than the colour of Christopher's skin.

They took off on the final leg to Kisumu, the wind increasing all the time and the aircraft 'crabbing' as the pilot followed his compass heading. Finally the township of Kisumu could be seen and as Tubs pointed it out to Christopher who shrieked with joy as he realised he would soon see his family again.

Flaps down, power off, the aircraft bounced gently on the grass. If nothing else, Flight Lieutenant Young was a good pilot. The navigator appeared at the door, shouting to Tubs, 'Be back here in two hours,' and looking over his shoulder in the direction of the pilot added, 'and for Christ's sake don't be late...'

They set off into downtown Kisumu, a settlement on the north-west edge of the impressive Lake Victoria. It was very hot and Christopher was now dripping with sweat and looking decidedly uncomfortable in his European suit and tie. Stopping at the first duka, Tubs bought a couple of beers and eyed his watch, fearful of being late back, even by a few minutes, knowing full well the mood of the pilot. The town resembled an old Western film set with its broken-down shops, bars and houses, each one seemingly propping the other one up. On the far side of the massive lake could be seen the paddle streamers that plied their trade by offering five-day trips to rich German and American tourists.

After a short walk down a dusty side street, they arrived at a concrete-built house with a roof of galvanised steel sheets.

Christopher leapt into the air and ran through the open doors. From the squeals of laughter that came from within almost instantly it was obviously going to be a happy visit. Christopher quickly introduced Tubs to his four sisters, who kissed him at the same time as thanking him for bringing their brother home, if even for a short time. The room was full of smiling Africans shaking his hand, and wondering at the smartness of Christopher, who looked resplendent in his European suit.

Family planning had not reached this part of Kenya and the introduction of Catholicism had not helped either, thought Tubs cynically. Christopher's sisters were all attractive, with smooth black skins. Dickie would certainly have been in his element in their company. Tubs produced his aged Rolliflex and took a family picture, quenching his thirst on a well-received bottle of Tusker, supplied by the youngest and most attractive of Christopher's sisters.

Very soon it was time to go and Tubs found himself once again plastered with kisses, some more passionate than others, from the sisters.

Wiping the lipstick from his face as he waved goodbye, he and Christopher began to retrace their steps, the African happy and whistling as he walked the dusty road back to the airfield. Tubs looked at his watch. Thank God, they had plenty of time. Christopher carefully carried a bag given to him by his mother, full of produce and gifts for his wife and family.

Arriving at the airfield they were pleasantly surprised to find Flight Lieutenant Young sitting on the steps of the Met Office looking friendly and relaxed.

'Having a nice day lads?' he queried.

'Yes, thank you, Sir,' replied Tubs, and he and Christopher headed for the bar.

After a few minutes the navigator waved to them to get aboard the aircraft and seemed in a hurry. All the freight had now been unloaded but as they fastened their seat belts Flight Lieutenant Young appeared in the doorway.

'Ryan, it's going to be bloody rough on the way back and I mean *rough* so keep your seat belts on all the time, OK?'

He disappeared, seemingly in a hurry. They taxied out and took off, heading for Nakuru, the aircraft frequently dipping and then climbing on the updraft. Towards Nakuru huge storm clouds were gathering over the lake. They climbed towards the clouds and the Twin Pioneer's wings began to bend, the fuselage creaked and the engines roared ferociously as the little plane battled its way through the storm.

Christopher's face began to show signs of apprehension and Tubs shouted to him, above the noise of the engines, to visit the chemical toilet 'if in doubt'. He pushed a couple of sick bags onto Christopher's knee. Through heavy rain and violent turbulence they landed at Nakuru, and with the engines still running a Colonel of the KAR boarded and the aircraft took off again to escape the storm.

But there was no escape. The weather worsened and the navigator came around to check all passenger seat belts.

'We'll be about half an hour through this and it might get even worse,' he said, shaking his head.

It did just that... Twenty minutes out of Nakuru the Colonel unceremoniously dived into his sick bag like a horse looking for hay, as the aircraft bucked and slewed in all directions in a manner designed to test the airframe to its maximum. Shortly afterwards Christopher's sweating face turned a horrible shade of black/green and he emptied his stomach of the Tusker and food so generously supplied by his family.

It was obvious that the Colonel and Christopher would both be in need of the toilet and Tubs pushed his African friend towards it, shouting, 'don't be too long'. As soon as he reappeared the Colonel rushed to replace him, as if playing some bizarre game of airborne musical chairs. Christopher, although ill, still laughed from time to time, perhaps with nerves, as the aircraft dropped alarmingly with each down-draft.

The thick cloud remained, darkening the inside of the aircraft, until they reached Gil Gil where, as if ordained by heaven, the sky cleared and the turbulence abated. The aircraft swept in low, landing on the grass strip at Gil Gil, the Colonel still closeted in the toilet. After landing he appeared, looking immaculate but ashen, and noticeably unsteady on his feet. Tubs helped him down the wooden steps and with a wave of thanks he boarded the waiting Land Rover.

Flight Lieutenant Young appeared, laughing.

'Christ, sorry about that lads, but it was bloody rough, even frightened *me.*'

On the ground at Gil Gil they watched as two corporals loaded three cases of medial supplies bound for Eastleigh into the freight space, their faces straining as they struggled with their weighty task.

'Probably anti-pox pills,' reflected Tubs.

The weather was fine but the wind was fresh and the battered windsock stood straight out like a poker. They embarked for the final leg to Eastleigh, Christopher now smiling happily, his previous sickness seemingly forgotten. Tubs checked the chemical toilet and collected the sick-bags, making sure that the interior of the aircraft was ultra-clean.

The short flight was perfect, with clear blue skies, as if welcoming them back to RAF Eastleigh. The time was 1300 hours. After landing and taxiing in, Christopher climbed out of the aircraft, carrying his bag of gifts from his family. Tubs shook his hand and sent him on his way. Flight Lieutenant Young was already in the Ops Room, discarding his flying suit.

'Many thanks for the flight, Sir' said Tubs sincerely.

'Sorry about this morning, Ryan...' he started. 'I live out in the country and two days ago a gang of Africans broke in and stole some of my chickens and when my Alsatian went for them they shot it,' he said remorsefully.

'The bastards,' thought Tubs. He had seen the dog in Flight Lieutenant Young's car from time to time around the Station and everyone knew how fond he was of the animal.

'I'm so sorry to hear that, Sir,' said Tubs, keen to leave the Flight Lieutenant to his sadness.

'Thank you, and you're always welcome to come along again.'

Tubs walked back to the Orderly Room to find a letter from SAC Weldon, his ex-Orderly Roommate, now in Kuwait. He seemed to be enjoying life in the Persian Gulf almost as much as at Eastleigh. The Wing Commander appeared at the door of the Orderly Room.

'Everything OK this morning Ryan?' he asked.

'No problems, Sir,' was the quick reply.

20. More Adventures

The Kenya Government elections were now in full swing and Nairobi was placed out of bounds to all personnel until further notice. At the beginning of the week when local African leaders were to hold their rallies, camp personnel were issued with steel helmets.

'Is this to piss in Flight?' Dickie quipped to the Supply Flight Sergeant, on signing for his.

'No, it's to put that bloody great head of yours in!' barked the Flight Sergeant, who was not known for his sense of humour.

Christopher had quickly recovered from his flight to Kisumu and Tubs had received a nice letter from the African's mother, thanking him for arranging the flight.

After a few more days of chest-thumping from the local political candidates the elections were over, with the two nationalist parties, KADU and KANO, returned with vast majorities.

The white farmers, after a few drinks in the Norfolk on Saturdays, would talk of leaving Kenya and spoke fondly of 'the old days' before the tide had turned towards African self-government. It would not be too long before the true Kenyans ran their own country, but Tubs was careful not to argue too sympathetic a case for this in the company of the heavily-built white farmers, well-lubricated with local liquor, who were usually to be found in the main bar of the Norfolk or

New Stanley Grill at weekends. Independence would come, as it had done in Tanganyika, and why shouldn't it?

It was now March and the long rains loomed ahead at the end of the month. On the fifteenth Wilson airport sponsored an air display and on hearing this Tubs asked Dickie,

'Going to fly with your queer pilot friend Maloney?'

The response was immediate but Tubs ducked the incoming fist before it landed.

The RAF's contribution to the air display was to be a demonstration by a Twin Pioneer of No.21 Squadron, featuring the aircraft's short take-off and landing capability, and they had scrounged a lift down to Wilson on the early morning flight. At 0700 next morning they found themselves strapped into the two seats at the rear of the aircraft. The rear door of the aircraft had been taken off. Squadron Leader Bishop was flying, being the senior pilot.

After taxiing out, he held the aircraft with the brakes whilst revving the engine to maximum power. On slipping the brakes, the aircraft shot forward as if power-launched from an aircraft carrier, and within the length of a cricket pitch they were airborne. Tubs and Dickie lay in their seats, watching the panoramic view through the opening where the door was usually fitted. Ten minutes later they landed at Wilson. The day was spent pleasantly in social drinking in the many marquees set out for this purpose, and soon it was time for the short flight back to Eastleigh.

The AOC's annual inspection was imminent and as Flying Wing HQ was to be visited everything that didn't move had to be cleaned, and everything that did had to be saluted! It was a manic time with the Wing Commander shouting constantly for files to ensure that the administration was up-to-date, and even the Flying Wing Adjutant could be seen polishing his desk and his office windows.

The parade, a shortened version of the UK model, was relatively straightforward, but the constant rehearsals were considered deadly boring by the young conscripts.

'After this parade I'm going to get pissed downtown,' said Dickie, throwing his shoe polish lid at the wall as a mark of defiance.

On the morning of the parade it rained for the first time in weeks. Prior to the march-on the Flight Commander made a speech.

'I will be walking behind the AOC on the inspection. As you are aware, I don't know all your names, so if he stops to talk to you and I say, "This is SAC Brown Sir," for Christ's sake don't say, "My name's not Brown Sir, it's Smith" – OK?'

The Flight Commander was a young flier and more than pissed-off with the parade and its ceremony. After the parade the good news came through over the tannoy that the next day would be a stand-down.

The day of the stand-down the long rains began with a vengeance and Tubs resorted to wearing a ground sheet, the only piece of RAF clothing guaranteed to keep a person dry in such torrential rain. The Flight Sergeant interfered very little in the day-to-day running of the Orderly Room, so

Tubs was more than surprised to see him bearing down on him carrying a large filing index.

'Ryan, there's a kite going to the UK tonight with a spare seat, and the Wing Commander said it would be a good PR move to let an Army chap go on it for a change.'

'That's fair enough,' replied Tubs. 'What he's asked is for you to pick one name out of this box-file for this free trip and we'll ring his section straight away to give him the good news.'

'OK,' said Tubs, his hand reaching into the box-file, his eyes tightly closed. But on pulling out the card he read out the name in disbelief.

'Lance Corporal Robinson, Military Police Section.'

It was the MP who had charged Dickie for being out of bounds.

Without a flicker of movement in his face the Flight Sergeant barked, 'This file index is out of date, he's been posted, pick another.'

Tubs was bursting to laugh. The second choice was a Private Duke and the Flight Sergeant immediately picked up the phone to give him the goods news of his UK flight. Turning to Tubs he said, 'Not a word of this to anybody,' adding, 'That'll teach the fucker to charge one of my lads!'

He strode out. 'Poor Lance Corporal Robinson,' thought Tubs, 'Charging Dickie just cost him the trip of a lifetime.'

He fought back a pretend tear…

Christopher the tea-boy was well-liked by all. He was always smiling and carried out his duties to the letter, willingly and pleasantly. Even the incoming pilots, their flying suits awash with sweat, would find time to talk to him and give him chocolate for his two children. The previous Christmas, the whole Wing had collected to buy him a new bicycle and clothes for his wife.

He lived in a small house close to the main gate, together with twenty-two other trusted Africans. At weekends he would go down into Nairobi where the street-wise Africans lived and talked of *Uhuru* – the times to come – when the Europeans had left and Jomo Kenyatta would be released from prison. On his more serious days he would say 'Kenya is a black people's country' and there were few who would disagree, save the Rhodesian Loadmaster who worked in the Ops Room. 'Independence will come and we will go home,' said Dickie, teasingly. Christopher would look hurt and say with feeling, 'No, you and Tubs must stay and be my friends forever.' In his own way, he meant it, and both of them found it touching, knowing that one day they would leave their beloved Kenya and possibly never return, and say good-bye to Christopher and his ever-smiling face forever.

Tubs lay on his pit contemplating life in general, staring at the smoke-stained ceiling and waiting for the NAAFI bar to open. He found it quite a pleasant occupation, akin to medi-tation. The banging as the bar grills were taken down galvanised him into action and he carefully checked the state of his finances whilst making his way to the bar. The RAF was paying him £3.10 shillings per week and although this did not appear a princely sum, it was still amazing how much NAAFI beer it could buy.

The Station Commander, a physical-fitness freak, although not obvious by his physical appearance, urged on by the Physical Education Officer, organised a cross-country, and despite strong pleas, Tubs and Dickie were entered for the event. The Adjutant, during his early-morning stroll around the Station, had noticed the pair running and had, in his own mind, high hopes of the pair doing well in the event. Whilst the event was not extremely athletic, since the course was only three and a half miles, it has to be remembered that the altitude was 5,500 feet, and fitness was at a premium due to the lack of oxygen at this height.

On the day in question Tubs set off steadily, pacing himself for the second circuit, knowing that the unwary few who started at a furious pace would not last out. Exhausted, sweat pouring from his body, he crossed the finishing line thirty-third out of the 127 finishers. Dickie was fifteen places behind, much to his disgust. No one was more pleased than the Adjutant, who, accompanied by his wife, treated them both to more than a fair share of Tusker.

Letters began to arrive on a regular basis from Layla, lovingly sealed with kisses and always ending with 'When are you coming to Mombo again?' Hopefully very soon, thought Tubs. The 'long rains' were now almost spent.

A plague of worms had arrived at Eastleigh. Hundreds of thousands lay on the perimeter track and up the side of the wooden billets. Half an inch in length, they had eaten local crops of corn but within a day the sun's rays cremated them, leaving their dried skins blowing in the late afternoon wind.

During the week, crews of Station Flight flying the Pembroke had been on dropping missions to the Northern Frontier District, using chemicals designed to 'make rain'. Cattle in this area were dying because of the drought and their African owners were facing starvation, so a Station collection was made to buy supplies, which would be dropped by the hard-working aircrews. Starvation was a plight never experienced but easily appreciated by the majority of service personnel and the collection grew daily as the situation in the NFD worsened. Tubs and Dickie felt great sympathy for those in need; if service life had done anything for them it seemed to have made them more compassionate and perhaps more understanding.

Whitsun weekend arrived and with the help of the MT section and one of their fleet of Land Rovers they found themselves driving the dusty path to Rimuruitia, the home of the legendary Carr Hartley and his big game farm.

The route was north via Naivasha, Gil Gil, Nakuru, and then, after a quick stop for a beer and a meal at Thomson's Falls, onto the big game farm. They made good time, the driver knowing the route well, and the one hundred and thirty miles passed quickly through a swirl of murram. On their arrival at Barry's Hotel, Thomson's Falls, the barman recognised them immediately and began quickly restocking his bar with bottles of Tusker. The temperature at Thomson's Falls was much cooler than Nairobi and sweaters were

hastily unpacked and donned. The road from here was re-
putedly the worst in Kenya and after a half-hour stop they
found it was to live up to its reputation.

Pulling off the murram track their driver stopped to con-
sult his map and pointing his grimy finger at a cross-drawn
on the road, confidently announced 'We're here.' The long
rains had eroded what was left of the track.

Luck was one their side as an ageing bus appeared and
Tubs waved it to stop. The MT driver went into deep conversation with the Asian driver of the bus. After a few
minutes the bus driver drove off, sounding his horn and
waving as he left.

'Good job I came prepared,' said the MT driver, pointing
to the compass hanging from a cord around his neck. Orien-
tating the stained map he placed the compass on the 'X' spot
and the needle swung northwest to a bearing which the MT
driver quickly wrote onto the back of his right hand.

'We just take this bearing across the bund for twelve miles
and we should be there,' he announced.

The vehicle shot forward, the tyres attempting to grip the
loose earth and the bottom of the multitude of potholes. The
ride was rough and the passengers were thrown around like
pebbles in a can.

'Keep looking out for a wooden sign,' shouted the driver.

Ten minutes later, out of his sweat-filled eyes, Tubs spotted the sign which simply said 'Beware of animals – you are
entering Carr Hartley's Big Game Farm'. Driving on, they

spotted a young white boy leaning against a hitching rail and drinking Fanta.

'Jambo mate,' shouted the MT driver, waving cheerfully and trying hard to hide his relief on reaching his destination. The boy sauntered over, his KD bleached by the sun, around his waist a gun belt and a .38 calibre handgun strapped by a thong to his thigh. He was no older than fourteen but the sun had weathered his face making him look older.

'You come to have a look around?' he queried, in a thick Kenyan accent. The driver nodded and the boy went on. 'OK, the animals are all fairly tame, even the lions, but I warn you if you go near the fence the guard dogs aren't and they will just tear you to pieces.' He wagged his finger at the driver.

They climbed out of the Land Rover their faces covered with murram and sweat; they were not a pretty sight. The boy began to walk towards the fence, carrying not only his sidearm but also a pump-action Savage shotgun, which he carried with ease, as if accustomed to it.

They started off towards the line of animals, followed closely by a tall African who, although smiling, looked ever watchful. In every direction were animals, with elephant and rhino walking in fields as cows might be seen in the UK.

Suddenly two cheetahs on a long chain confronted them and both Tubs and Dickie stepped back, fearful for their lives. The MT driver hid behind the tall African to escape the inquisitive stare of the largest of the cheetahs. The African laughed and, walking up to the cheetahs, lay down alongside the female and began kissing the animal's face.

'You next, come along...' he gesticulated to Dickie.

Dickie was not too sure, but after a few seconds hesitation he stood beside the cheetah and patted its head as if it were a pet Labrador.

They moved on to where they encountered, lying in the grass, feeding on a bone, the largest lion Tubs had ever seen. The African stepped forward.

'This is Brutus; you've probably seen him in the American series 'African Life'. He really is world famous and whenever American film producers want a lion to wrestle, Brutus gets the work as he just loves to wrestle.' And on these words the African did just that, wrestling with the huge lion, the animal holding his shoulders and roaring impressively.

To see was to believe that wild animals raised from birth could respond to man's affection in this way.

'Come on,' said the African, and each member of the party knelt down alongside the huge lion to record on film the event for posterity.

Carr Hartley had trained, not without great personal danger, a considerable number of wild animals not to be afraid of man. The animals rarely roamed, as they treated the park as their natural home, and perhaps even saw themselves as part of the Carr Hartley family.

Soon, they were in sight of an ominous fence and they could hear the frenzied barking of the guard dogs.

'I think we'll turn round and go back now,' said Dickie, in mock fear. Passing the long line of animals again they took more photographs before the position of the sun in the Kenya sky made them mindful that it was time to leave.

Shaking the African's hand and warmly thanking him for the tour, Tubs pressed some money into his hand before climbing aboard the Land Rover. The white boy had seemingly disappeared, until turning the corner at the end of the track, they spotted him and cheerfully shouted 'thank you' from the back-flap of the Land Rover. He smiled and waved his shotgun in the air enthusiastically as they disappeared from view.

Tubs and Dickie slept all the way back to Eastleigh, tired and happy with their day's adventure.

The MT driver dropped them off at West Site with a friendly 'See you in the NAAFI lads' and drove off into the darkness along the perimeter track.

21. Search and Rescue

A friendly inbound Hastings pilot would, from to time, bring in recent English newspapers for the benefit of the Ops Room members. On reading a recent 'leader' in the *Daily Express*, Tubs was aghast to see that it told of mass riots in Nairobi and hinted that all whites were in danger of being murdered as they slept.

Admittedly Mau Mau oathing had taken place at Nakuru and a few white settlers had been murdered, but these cases were very rare and occurred only in isolated regions. On outlying farms the European farmers were carrying weapons, but this was only a precaution from bandits. Tubs wrote home, mentioning the article, as his father was an avid reader of the *Daily Express*, advising him that its author must have been on some sort of hallucinatory drug when it was written. Once again, the media had got it wrong.

To his abject horror, Tubs found himself on parade duty for the Queen's Birthday at Government House. As a result, along with other unfortunate victims, every morning he had to practise marching, complete with rifle, fixed bayonet, white webbing and white gloves. To begin with he felt extreme resentment, he hated drill, but as time passed the drill became easier and the feeling passed. The day finally came for the parade and, after a few hours rehearsal, he found himself in the centre of Nairobi, marching along to stirring music and, to his amazement, enjoying himself as he executed the complex drill movements. On returning to the billet to rid himself of his white webbing Dickie walked in.

'Blow me if it's not the next British Ambassador to Kenya,' he declared, collapsing on the bed in laughter.

Tubs yearned to return to Mombasa and the arms of Layla, but the work rate in the Orderly Room had risen to fever pitch after a large section of the admin staff had been posted to Bahrain and Kuwait. The final straw came when his impending weekend leave was cancelled. The weekend came quickly and he and Dickie just went about their normal chores, cleaning shoes, spraying the mosquito net with anti-bug spray, and generally tidying up what was, to them, their 'home'.

Sunday arrived and Tubs lay in his pit, focussing his eyes on the ceiling, as a small lizard ran across the water pipe. Suddenly his mosquito net was swept aside and Dickie stood there.

'Get a move on you dozy bastard,' he shouted, 'we're going to Mombasa!'

'When for Christ's sake?' asked Tubs, wiping the sweat from his face with a handkerchief.

'They're starting the engines now and the Land Rover's outside to take us to 21 Squadron,' said Dickie, throwing a pair of trousers to his friend.

Tubs had never dressed so fast in his life. Cleaning his teeth and washing his face he was urged on by Dickie's voice and the engine of the awaiting Land Rover. They ran towards it, leapt in, and with a roar the vehicle shot off down the perimeter track towards the apron on which was parked the Twin Pioneer of 21 Squadron. Dickie breathlessly began to explain.

'There's fucking hell on down there. 70 Squadron have to fly a Beverley tonight to Aden and the Master Engineer has gone down to Mombasa on leave without giving his wife an address where he can be contacted. The Master Engineer's wife has stayed behind with her sister, who is over from the UK. He gave his name and address to the Ops Room for contact as The Nyali Beach Hotel, but when the Wing Commander telephoned last night they said he hadn't checked in, nor was he booked in. There's a rumour going around the Squadron that he's shacked up with some *bibi*, but God knows where – it's a big town, Mombasa.'

They reached the aircraft and quickly clambered aboard whereupon the Twin Pioneer, taking the shortest route, headed into the wind and was quickly airborne. They had been flying for approximately thirty minutes when the navigator appeared and beckoned the six passengers forward. Although shouting above the roar of the engines, his tone was secretive.

'Look… we've been sent down to Mombasa to find Master Engineer Ellis, who has *got* to be on a Beverley flight to Aden tonight. The naughty boy is not where he told his wife he was going to be, and this means, quite frankly, that he could be in any bar, brothel, or God knows where in Mombasa. When we get there we'll split up and I'll give you a telephone number to call if anyone should find him. Here's a recent picture of him.' He held up a photograph of a short, fat man with a moustache. 'Remember, one thing. We're all men of the world, so no matter where you find him or with whom, we forget the fact, OK?'

The party nodded in agreement and returned to their seats. Under full power the aircraft made good headway and they found themselves walking through the arrivals lounge at Mombasa after just two and a half hours flying, with the temperature relatively cool at 79 degrees. Each of the six passengers was given a special route to cover in the search for the errant Master Engineer.

They set off in a lorry, to be dropped off one by one, each feeling like a huntsman without horse.

'Bet you a beer I find the lucky bastard first,' shouted Dickie, as he leapt from the tailboard of the lorry. Tubs was last to be dropped off and immediately scanned the street for a fat white man with a moustache, but to no avail. The arrangement was to be back at the world-famous 'Tusks' in Kilindini Road at 1700 hours. He set off, walking briskly, writing each street's name on a sheet of paper to prove his vigilance. Two blocks away he could see the battered sign of The New Bristol Hotel swaying in the light breeze and he made his way hurriedly towards it, eager for a sight of Layla.

Reaching the main door he peered through the faded wooden slats and could see Layla polishing the bar tables. At first, she did not notice his presence, but then she caught sight of him out of the corner of her eye.

'Tubs!' she shrieked, and ran towards him.

They kissed passionately and hugged like two brown bears.

'I'm afraid that I have little time,' said Tubs, ever mindful of his duty. 'I, or rather we, have got to find this bastard.' He held the photograph of the missing Master Engineer before her eyes. She looked at it closely.

'He hasn't been in here,' she confirmed. 'What has he done, robbed a bank?'

'No, worse than that... at least, if his wife finds out!' said Tubs, laughing.

Layla went to find the owner of the bar and asked permission to take a couple of hours off. He did not mind, as she was a good worker.

'We've got to visit every bar, show them the photo, and hope that someone knows where he is,' said Tubs, taking Layla's eager hand as they walked into the sunlit street.

Layla knew many bars that Tubs was not familiar with and soon they had visited fourteen of them, but without any luck. Tubs was not really surprised. He imagined that the Master Engineer was happily tucked up in a hotel bed somewhere on the outskirts of Mombasa, presumably with his girlfriend. His stomach told him that it was lunchtime so they headed for The Carlton Hotel, which was noted for its crab and lobster salad and was a pleasant and popular watering hole.

When they arrived they were not surprised to find the restaurant and bar full. The salad was served and they both ceased talking and waded into it. In the bar were a mixture of nationalities, Asians, Germans, Japanese, and of course black and white Kenyans. As his eyes searched the bar Tubs' gaze fell on a young *bibi* in her mid-twenties, wearing a very short skirt. She wore heavy make-up, wore high heels and there was little doubt in Tubs' mind of her profession. She looked restless, as if waiting for someone. They finished the salad and sat back to relax in the leather chairs, and as he did so, Tubs saw, moving towards him, a short, fat white man wearing baggy shorts, with brown open-toed sandals to match his ensemble.

He staggered slightly and as he reached the young *bibi* he kissed her neck teasingly. Tubs froze and reached into his pocket for the photograph, but before he had even looked at it he knew that this man was the missing Master Engineer.

'Christ,' he thought, 'what do I do now?'

The couple at the bar were now holding onto each other, or rather she was holding him to stop him falling off the bar stool. Tubs sensed that it was not a good time or place to advise a drunken SNCO of his duty to the RAF or to his wife and children. Many of the lunchtime eaters were now looking at the couple and it was obvious that the *bibi* was trying to get her male companion to leave before he collapsed. She continued to nestle his cheek whilst his hand fondled her leg.

Tubs strode over to the phone and quickly dialled the Nyali number.

'Mombasa Operations,' a gruff voice answered, which he was pleased to recognise as the navigator's.

'It's SAC Ryan. I've found the Master Engineer at The Carlton Hotel. The bad news is two-fold. Firstly, he's pissed out of his skull, and secondly he's in tow with a *bibi*.'

There was a long pause and then his instructions, short and sweet.

'Give Ellis a drink and keep him there. I'll be there in fifteen minutes.'

He returned to Layla, who, like many others in the bar was watching the antics of the Master Engineer, who was now openly groping the *bibi*, his other hand grasping a large tumbler of gin. Tubs slouched over, purposely knocking Ellis's drink out of his hand. The burly Master Engineer turned around, looking startled.

'Easy mate,' he said, his eyes looking weary.

'Have another drink, mate,' slurred Tubs.

'Yes, might as well,' said the errant engineer.

'My name's Ryan, my friends call me Tubs, and this a friend of mine called Layla.'

The fat man's hand shot out and he replied, 'Mine's Harry Ellis and this little friend is called Nina,' he laughed hysterically.

They shook hands, Layla eyeing the 'working girl' with mounting disapproval. The combination of Nina's strong perfume and Ellis's body odour overpowered Tubs, and the bar staff were now eyeing the Master Engineer with contempt as, try as he might, he could not manage the bar stool and was now slumped over the bar. Tubs prayed that the navigator would soon appear

Ellis ordered another round of drinks and at first the barman was hesitant, but Tubs winked knowingly at him and he relented. At long last he heard the Land Rover screech to a halt outside and watched the long strides of the uniformed navigator as he swept through the swing doors.

Slapping Ellis on the shoulder he chided, 'What's my favourite Master Engineer doing in a place like this? Naughty boy didn't give us the right address so we've had to come in an air-taxi to take you back for the Aden flight tonight.'

Ellis was too far gone to fully comprehend the situation, but slowly years of military discipline and intuition told him that duty called. The wily navigator bought yet another round of drinks and began to talk to Layla until suddenly he declared, 'I think it's about time for you and me to return to the airfield, don't you Harry?'

Ellis was beginning to grasp the situation, if loosely, and without hesitation replied, 'Anything you say, Sir.'

Tubs and the navigator helped Ellis off the stool and steered him through the door towards the awaiting Land Rover. On reaching it the navigator said, 'Look, he's legless Ryan, I can't fly him back in this state. I'll take him back to the airfield and sober him up and then slip back and pick you up at The Tusks in Kilindini Road at 1700 hours. OK?'

Tubs' face showed his appreciation of this idea. With considerable difficulty they lifted the huge bulk of Ellis into the back seat of the Land Rover, with the *bibi* still holding his arm affectionately like a child with a favourite teddy bear. In a cloud of murram the Land Rover departed, leaving the three of them at the roadside. With a smile and a wiggle of her posterior, the *bibi* disappeared into the afternoon shopping crowd to look for another punter and Layla and Tubs went back to the bar to buy the barman a drink and thank him for his understanding manner.

The barman, smiling philosophically told them, 'The fat man he always stays with that bibi when he comes to Mombasa.'

Layla and Tubs left hand-in-hand. Tired and dehydrated, they hailed a taxi and headed for Layla's house on the outskirts of Mombasa. Layla's mother had a prestigious job in an Asian bank in the centre of town and would not be home until early evening. Layla's room was neat, with woven mats adorning its stone floors, and the shelves contained many books, including the complete works of William Shakespeare. The only sound came from the gently whirring fan in the ceiling.

Tubs walked towards Layla and held her. The smell of jasmine invaded his nostrils, the softness of her skin exciting him and increasing his desire. She wore a simple pink dress and slowly, as if mesmerised, he undid the buttons, whilst she removed his shirt and kissed his chest. She removed his socks and trousers as if he were a child and soon they lay together naked on the white cotton sheets.

For a few moments they savoured the anticipation. Her hands lovingly touched his body and his followed the gentle curves of her smooth scented skin until, overcome with passion, he slowly entered her. Their bodies moved in unison and for a few minutes they knew the hedonistic pleasure of sex and love entwined as one.

Their passion spent and their bodies satisfied, they dressed again, kissing each other affectionately and often. Tubs glanced at his watch. For once, time was on his side. There was still time for a leisurely walk back to Kilindini Road and to sit on one of the many seats and watch the world go by. They sat there together, holding hands, at peace with the world and deliriously happy.

At 1700 hours the Land Rover appeared, driven by the now smiling navigator. Tubs kissed Layla, whispering 'see you in a few weeks' and jumped in the front seat of the Land Rover, waving to her until she disappeared from view as the vehicle roared back towards the airfield.

'Hope you had a good afternoon,' said the navigator, with a knowing smile. One by one they picked up the rest of the six passengers. Dickie was the last to be picked up and looked as if he had enjoyed himself. His face was ashen, a shade it took on, for some reason, perhaps known only to a doctor, when he had consumed a massive dose of alcohol.

Soon they arrived at the airfield and boarded the Twin Pioneer. Harry, the elusive Flight Engineer, now relatively sober, was the last to board.

'Nice to meet you all and thanks for coming down,' he said, cheerfully. The aircraft was soon airborne and climbing steeply into the clear blue sky. Eastleigh Ops had been advised that the Flight Engineer has been located and that the midnight flight to Aden was 'on'. Over Tsavo and Amboselli game parks the pilot flew low, down to 100 feet at times, to chase a herd of zebra. After this low-level flying he resumed his cruising altitude and the passengers settled back into their seats. Harry produced a bag and offered around slices of pineapple, presumably carefully cut by him.

Soon the aircraft began its descent into Eastleigh and Harry, to his credit, changed his gin-stained and crumpled shirt for a new nylon one carefully tied a double Windsor knot in his 70 Squadron tie. He looked sober, fit and presentable. The aircraft landed with a rumble of the wheels and slew round as if saluting the Group Captain sitting in his car beneath the starboard wing.

Harry was the first to disembark, looking cheerful and relaxed. He stood smartly to attention as he met the awaiting Group Captain and Tubs listened fascinated as he casually said, 'Sorry, you couldn't find me sir, but I caught food poisoning the first day of my leave and booked into a hotel near the military hospital in case I had to be admitted. Didn't want to worry the family, you understand.'

The Group Captain replied with a wry smile.

'We all have our problems, Mr. Ellis, don't we?'

Tubs put his hand over his mouth to stop himself from laughing out loud and quickly disembarked. As they ducked under the wing the navigator appeared.

'Ryan, don't forget our secret,' he said sternly, adding with a laugh, 'From what I hear food-poisoning is the least of his worries!'

It had been another good day.

22. Kilimanjaro

A rumour had reached Dickie via the SATCO that RAF were about to sponsor another climbing expedition. The mountain to be climbed on this occasion being Mount Kilimanjaro. A party of twelve was to be chosen and it became obvious to Tubs that this would be his last chance of sponsorship before his demob. Both Dickie and Tubs decided that this was an opportunity not to be missed. The RAF sponsored the expedition to a maximum of eight hundred Kenya shillings, a huge amount of money if you were a conscript.

The porters, so important for a successful climb, received five shillings a day per man and the guides, due to their years of experience, seven shillings and sixpence a day. Surplus money was spent on accommodation at the huts en route and travel to the starting point.

Tubs considered himself quite fit, having toned his body by daily running and reduced his weight to a lean one hundred and forty seven pounds. On meeting the PFO one day when collecting his mail, Tubs plied him with reasons why he and Dickie should be considered for places on the list of climbers. The PFO, impressed by his keenness, advised him of the meeting to be held one evening in the week when the names for the climb would be decided.

Arriving early for the meeting, held in a disused hangar at the bottom end of 21 Squadron's site, Tubs and Dickie positioned themselves on the front row of seats. On a noticeboard behind a table was a blank blackboard on which the chosen names would be written. The climb itself was not difficult or dangerous from a mountaineering point of view, but demanded peak fitness, for it involved a walk of seventy miles to the peak and back at very high altitude, placing heavy demands on the body due to lack of oxygen. This critical factor had proved to be the downfall of many would-be climbers in the past.

The expedition required careful planning, down to the last detail, and the equipment was checked and rechecked. Sleeping bags, rations, snow goggles, string vests and heavy-duty pullovers were but a few of the items on the long list necessities. The Flight Sergeant in Admin Wing had offered to loan Tubs a pair of sheepskin-lined flying boots.

Without ceremony the meeting got under way. The audience numbered in excess of fifty, and after a short introduction, the PFO began to speak, his voice clear and loud as if remembering his Cranwell days.

'I've already found a leader who has been to the top before and I've put three on the list who failed on the last climb, so there's only eight places left, I'm afraid. Anybody who I don't consider fit will not be accepted. What I want now is a show of hands who want to go and I'll take it from there.'

Tubs and Dickie shot their hands in the air, and the PFO began to take the names. There were thirteen volunteers for the eight places. The PFO started again.

'OK. I'll accept that all these candidates are pretty fit as I've seen most of them running, and so I'll pick those with little time to do in Kenya, and the rest can go on the next claim list, OK.' The audience nodded. 'OK. If I call out your name please stay behind after the meeting.'

Tubs was the first name called but Dickie's was omitted and added to the next climb list. The meeting ended as quickly as it had started and soon Tubs met his fellow climbers whilst Dickie dejectedly made his way to the NAAFI.

Kilimanjaro is not only the highest mountain in Africa, but also the highest freestanding mountain anywhere in the world. To climb it at the RAF's expense seemed too good a chance to miss. The PFO advised all of them to run six miles a day at a leisurely pace or to do some circuit training in the gym as a replacement measure.

Tubs hated circuit training; it reminded him of Bridgnorth and its concentration camp atmosphere he had hated so intensely. He stopped drinking beer and drank spirits instead, and his weight dropped to one hundred and forty pounds.

At 0600 the following Wednesday the twelve met outside the PFO's office and carefully loaded the ageing Armstrong Siddeley transport with their precious equipment and stores and set off for Moshi, Tanganyika, a 250-mile journey on unknown and unmarked roads and tracks. It soon became apparent that the vehicle was not an ideal choice. Murram poured in through the windscreen and doors whenever they travelled at any speed and the heat inside the vehicle was unbearable. The other two vehicles, Land Rovers, were custom-made for the purpose, and with the canvas roof flaps down there was sufficient air to keep the passengers cool.

The journey seemed endless and it was a tired team that eventually arrived at The Marangu Hotel to find the bar overflowing with tourists resplendent in their newly-purchased safari suits. The party ate a meal in the darkened dining room of the hotel, apprehensive of what lay ahead, all wondering if they had the physical and mental strength to succeed. The silence was ominous, they were all saving every ounce of strength for the days ahead.

At dawn next day, after a restless night, Tubs and his fellow climbers set off for Bismark Hut, nine thousand feet up, and a ten mile walk up steep, rough, ground. This stage was made without undue effort and although the bunks at Bismark were uncomfortable the hut itself was spick and span.

That night they met a party of climbers, who had reached the summit and were on the descent, trying hard not to listen to their tales of sickness, headache and dizziness as they approached the peak. Waking up in a frozen sleeping bag, Tubs contemplated another hard day as dawn broke and he set off alone, walking and then climbing alone. His unappetising breakfast comprised dry toast and baked beans, but he ate it, knowing its energy content. His climb took him across arid plains and the occasional stream. At times he would meet smiling Africans, urging him on and wishing him good luck, and at this stage he was pleased with his progress and his level of fitness.

However, the next day, after another restless night and biting cold, the climb became much steeper and the terrain rougher, making Tubs pant heavily for the first time. Towards the middle of the afternoon he passed one of his fellow climbers, looking pale and resting every few hundred yards. Tubs took some of his provisions from him and carried them for him, but he continued to pant ominously, and lean heavily on his climbing stick. These sticks, carried awkwardly on the first day, became more and more necessary as the terrain became rougher.

Late in the afternoon Tubs and the other climber reached Kibo Hut, at fifteen thousand feet up, and for the first time, the couple experienced the pain of headache caused by lack of oxygen. Tubs did not feel hungry and his headache became worse. Four of the party were sick, their faces ashen, and their hands trembling with the cold, despite the thick gloves.

The worst was yet to come. At 0145 Tubs was rudely awakened by the senior guide, grinning as if he alone was enjoying the experience, who inquired, 'Habari?'. Tubs had hardly found the strength to reply when he noticed the guide had gone. He stood up and surveyed his surroundings, a dirty wooden and corrugated-iron hut with an evil-smelling paraffin lamp hanging from the ceiling. His head ached and his stomach begged for food, which he knew he would not be able to keep down. Taking a thermometer from his pocket he wondered how he could have managed to sleep in thirty-six degrees of frost. He could hear his fellow climbers moving around in the next room of the hut.

They assembled outside, a party of shuffling, miserably cold figures, each hanging onto a climbing stick and ready to start the long agonising haul to Gilman's Point, nineteen thousand feet up. The grinning senior guide set off, now hated by the entire party for his resilience to the altitude and extreme cold. They looked up but could see nothing in the darkness except the swinging of his paraffin lamp as he cajoled and bullied them to keep up the pace he dictated.

God, how they hated him!

Above them lay three thousand feet of almost vertical frozen screen. The wind howled and the freezing cold bit like a surgeon's knife into Tubs' Vaseline-protected face. They climbed on, almost hypnotised by the swinging lamp ahead.

The senior guide shouted down to increase the pace but there was little response. At seventeen thousand feet three of the party were very sick and lost all sense of balance. Despite the cajoling of the guide they turned back, three sad, lonely figures, drained mentally and physically by the cruelty of the mountain. Every muscle in Tubs' body was now screaming. At seventeen and a half thousand feet he found that he could only take half a dozen steps before being overcome by the lack of oxygen and having to rest on his climbing stick. Even the toughest of the party were now finding the going totally exhausting, after days of hard climbing and little sleep.

At eighteen thousand nine hundred feet, Tubs passed the grave of an Austrian climber who had fallen to his death from the rocks above. He rallied himself mentally. Light burned his eyes through the snow goggles, but he realised he was nearly there. He peered at his watch and saw that they had been climbing for four hours. After another fifteen minutes of agony they reached Gilman's Point, where the smiling senior guide awaited them. Every step now felt to Tubs as if he was being strangled slowly. They rested for ten minutes, a tired dishevelled group now, urged on by the guide to start the final ascent to the highest peak of the mountain – Kaiser Wilhelm Spitze – named by the German climbers Meyer and Purtscheller in 1889.

Tubs climbed on, now confident of success, his tiredness being overtaken by a feeling of elation. At last he stood with the others at the highest point and peered down into the crater as if mesmerised by the scene below – huge pillars of ice set in a square with icicles hundreds of feet long on all sides.

Each of the party took photographs and signed the book hidden carefully in the snow. How odd, Tubs thought, that he should be so high above every one of the millions of people going about their lives on the continent of Africa.

Soon the guide gathered them together like lost sheep and beckoned them to start the descent to escape the freezing cold, and abate their headaches. At every downward step their legs appeared less leaden and the air more exhilarating. Slipping and sliding down the deep volcanic scree, they made good time eager to reach Bismark Hut, and were able to eat and wash again.

Having been pushed to the absolute physical limits, the group were now cheerful, but could only feel sorry for those who had failed to withstand the lack of oxygen. They were now descending quite rapidly, herded together like tired cattle, footsore and eager to get to base camp. On their arrival at Bismark the porters mysteriously disappeared, but later returned with laurels of everlasting flowers, which they placed ceremoniously around the safari hats of the team.

The next stop was The Marangu Hotel and the warmth and hospitality of the bar to celebrate. They walked on, heads down, desperately tired until in the distance could be seen the welcome sight of the white walls of the hotel.

On arriving, they headed straight for the baths to cleanse themselves of the sweat, dust and dirt clinging to their bodies like a second skin. Tubs noticed his feet were badly blistered, with large areas of skin hanging from the soles of his feet, and he quickly borrowed a tin of salt to add to the bathwater. He could never remember a bath feeling so good. He felt almost reborn as he dried his now lean body.

A steak meal had been ordered for all the party and after this and a few bottles of red wine they had an early night, weariness still very much in their bodies. Tubs could not remember going to bed but raised by the leader's shout at daybreak he quickly dressed and packed his small rucksack. After a hearty breakfast, supplied free of charge by the kind hotel management, they boarded their vehicles and headed south to Eastleigh.

The Armstrong Siddeley's engine overheated every few hours, forcing them to stop and allow it to cool down, making the 250-mile drive seem endless, but as they approached Nairobi the quality of the roads improved and they were able to make good time for the final stage of their journey. Very tired, but happy, they unloaded the vehicles at Eastleigh.

On arrival the PFO greeted them and appeared to be delighted with their success.

Tubs made his way back to the billet and made for the shower to wash away the thick covering of murram he had acquired en route. Pulling on his slacks he went in search of Dickie, and found him, predictably, in the NAAFI bar, practising his Swahili on the barman.

'Well done!' said Dickie, on hearing of Tubs' success, adding, 'Get this Tusker inside you my old mate.'

'It was a bloody sight harder than I thought it would be,' Tubs admitted, humbly.

After a few drinks he left Dickie with his Swahili lesson and returned to the billet where fatigue swept over him. He carefully placed the everlasting flowers given to him by the porters at Bismark Hut into a bag for safekeeping and then, after slumping on the bed still clothed, he fell into a long and deep sleep...

23. Firearms Training

News arrived via incoming aircrews that conditions for those on detachment in Kuwait were far from good. They spoke of hundreds of men sleeping in one hangar, of poor food, no entertainment and temperatures reaching 160 degrees at midday.

For a change of routine, Tubs and Dickie travelled into Nairobi on the bus. The bus had a two-fare structure, very cheap on the top deck, where the majority of the passengers were African, and expensive on the lower deck, accommodating mostly Asian and European passengers. On both decks the banter was noisy, incessant and, to say the least, cosmopolitan. They arrived at Nairobi Bus Depot amidst a thronging mass of passengers and quickly made their way to the comfortable surroundings of the New Stanley Grill.

After a couple of drinks they left and walked down Elliott Street, where Dickie hailed a passing taxi. Pushing Tubs inside he explained, 'I know a nice little bar just a mile from here…'

'Oh for Christ's sake, we're not going out of bounds again are we?' asked Tubs, becoming irritated.

'No way! This is just on the highway, still in bounds but a fair walk,' explained Dickie.

The bar was full and the owner, immaculately dressed in a mohair suit, dashed over upon seeing Dickie, who promptly ordered the 'house special' – spiced chicken. Tubs was puzzled as to how Dickie had found this unusual cosmopolitan bar when he noticed a very tall African girl descending the stairs and smiling in their direction.

Noticing Tubs' expression Dickie said through clenched teeth, as he returned the girl's smile, 'She just loves white men.' Dickie stood up, forever the gentleman, and kissed her lightly on the cheek, saying 'Fancy meeting you here, Tanya, meet my good friend Tubs.' Tubs extended his hand, which was small for a man's, and her hand enveloped his completely, her long, brightly-painted nails scratching at his skin. He sat like the proverbial gooseberry, watching Dickie gaze into her eyes, his right arm holding her tiny waist.

'How long have you known Dickie?' she asked, eager to be polite.

'Too bloody long,' thought Tubs!

'Oh a very long time,' he answered, with a smile, and waited for the next move. He did not have to wait long.

'Just going upstairs for a few minutes to listen to one of Tanya's new records,' announced Dickie, in his best choirboy voice. Tubs did not reply and watched with amusement as they climbed the wooden stairs, her eyes gazing into his.

The owner came from the reception desk and delivered a tray of drinks.

'Hi, my name's Jake,' he said. Tubs thought it an unusual name, under the circumstances, but he was not there to argue. 'You met my fine daughter?' Jake queried.

'Christ,' thought Tubs, 'Dickie has been drinking his beer all night and now he's screwing his daughter.' Jake seemed unconcerned as to his daughter's whereabouts and more interested in talking horseracing and seeking Tubs' opinion of Brian Jago's mounts. After a short while he returned to his duties, ordering another tray of drinks before departing.

A few moments later Dickie appeared, nonchalantly tying his tie as he descended the stairs, his face looking like the cat that just devoured the cream. Sexual activity had made Dickie hungry again and he ordered another portion of spiced chicken, which he proceeded to devour like a hungry lion. Tanya had disappeared and, as they left, Jake shook their hands enthusiastically.

'Now you know where to find *bibis* with a bit of class. If it's good enough for the Rhodesian Police Inspector, then it's good enough for me.'

Tubs was speechless.

Hailing a taxi, Dickie looked like a man who had enjoyed himself. Full of spiced chicken, free beer and the recent services of an attractive bibi, his face radiated a sense of achievement. Paying off the taxi they climbed over the high wire fence at West Site instead of taking the long walk via the main gate.

'One day,' whispered Tubs, 'some trigger-happy guard is going to blow our balls off when we're halfway up this fence.'

'Bollocks' came the speedy reply.

The next day Tubs was solemnly advised by the SWO's office that he had less than six months to serve, and rummaging through his belongings, he found his passport, showing a scowling airman in a civilian jacket. He smiled as he threw it into the back of his locker drawer…

Thursday came and Dickie had arranged a late breakfast for both of them after they were to walk the mile to the mess along the perimeter track.

All airmen stationed at Eastleigh had to endure, annually, the rigours of the Ground Defence School, which consisted of a series of films about fire, safety and weapons training, with the final three days spent on the firing range under the ever-watchful eye of the RAF Regiment. The slightest error in procedure was rewarded with a torrent of obscenities. Bruised shoulders and deafness from the hours constant gunfire was the norm. Dickie, tired from the heat and bored with the course, committed a cardinal sin by failing to pull the heavy .303 rifle fully into his shoulder, and paid the penalty with a bloody nose when the weapon recoiled.

On seeing the blood running from his face the Flight Sergeant rushed over, screaming at the top of his generous voice.

'You fuckin' tosser, you're doing more damage to yourself than the enemy would!' Snatching the rifle from Dickie's hand he placed it on his hip and proceeded to rapid-fire, slipping the bolt, inserting another round hitting the man-sized target with speed and accuracy every time.

After a further two days Tubs and Dickie qualified as RAF Marksman on the LMG and .303 rifle, but not until having suffered much derision and cajoling from the Flight Sergeant in charge. On the final day of the course the Flight Sergeant arrived in his Land Rover with six weapons, spotlessly clean and shining with newly-applied gun oil.

'Clean these,' he commanded, placing the weapons on the firing point table.

Slowly, and carefully they polished the working parts and furniture with the '4 x 2' until they shone in the sun.

At 0900 the Flight Sergeant returned and began to inspect the weapons, a mock look of distain appeared on his face, quickly followed by a smile.

'OK, you can fuck off now, but don't go back to your sections, and remember if anyone wants to know you were here all day.'

They skulked back to West Site, taking the long way back to their billet, ignoring the call of the NAAFI bar, and together they spent the rest of the day writing home and soaking up the sun on the wooden veranda of the block.

Tubs wrote to Layla that he hoped to be in Mombasa again, but realising that he would have to return to the UK very soon. At times he felt as if there was an egg timer in his head, with the sands of Kenya ebbing slowly away…

24. *A Romantic Rendezvous*

Tubs had just three days leave left and had no doubt as to where he was going to spend it – Mombasa and the Nyali Beach Hotel. Dickie was tasked to find a flight and, after a few days, he duly found his friend a seat on a 70 Squadron Beverley training flight to Mombo. Tubs wrote to Layla, advising her of his forthcoming leave. The days passed uneventfully with many hours spent at the swimming pool as flying was cut back to training flights only.

Soon Tubs found himself packing the overnight bag given him by his brother before he left the UK, now looking suitably worn. Flying with 70 Squadron was extremely convenient, as their aircraft were parked only two hundred yards from the billets at West Site. On a clear day, with the dawn breaking at the end of the peri-track, Tubs climbed, once again, the horizontal ladder into the passenger section of the giant Beverley and strapped himself in. Slowly, the engines, one by one, roared into action, the pilot testing their power while holding the aircraft on its brakes. On the third of the four engines there was a delay, followed by a crackle through the intercom as the pilot announced irritably,

'We've got a mag drop on number three engine.'

Tubs had told Layla to be at the airfield at 0930 and cursed his bad luck. By the sound of his voice the pilot was not happy either. Maybe he had a date in Mombasa too…

From the window Tubs could see ladders appear and frantic engine fitters ascended, armed with tools and torches, peered into the engine cowling and began to tinker within. After ten minutes or so the airmen descended, the ladders came down and the Flight Sergeant i/c ground crew gave an encouraging thumbs-up sign.

The pilot quickly taxied across the short peri-track and lined up the aircraft for take-off. He revved the formerly unserviceable engine, and then all four together, the Beverley straining on the brakes like an angry bull, snorting with rage. Then the two words Tubs longed to hear came through the intercom. 'Clear, take-off.'

With an almighty roar and clouds of murram dust surrounding the fuselage, the Beverley leapt forward and eased its way into the clear blue sky. One of Tubs jobs during the flight was to make coffee for the aircrew and this duty he had perfected even in turbulence. Climbing down the vertical ladder with the tray of coffees, he walked agilely across the lower floor and climbed upwards into the cockpit, where he found the crew relaxed and reading local newspapers, the aircraft safely in the hands of the automatic pilot, having reached cruising altitude.

'We'll make up the lost time as we've got a strong tail wind,' said the pilot, anticipating Tubs' question, and adding, 'I'm going to do two or three 'touch and go' landings at Mombasa, so don't get frightened.' The idea was to give the co-pilot a chance to practise his landings with the aircraft touching down but then immediately taking off again with full power applied. The exercise would then be repeated as many times as the pilot felt necessary.

Soon the co-pilot started his descent, the aircraft lurching to either side as he fought to keep it on the white line, with the effects of the wind shear plaguing his efforts. At the end of the runway he banked alarmingly and came in again, this time his new-found skill being rewarded with a perfect landing. The Beverley taxied to the front of the airport lounge, and without delay the engines were closed down, one by one, and the propellers feathered.

Tubs almost ran down the steps and found, to his delight, facing him, her nose pressed against the airport lounge window, Layla. She wore a simple blue cotton dress, and her hair had grown almost to her waist. Slowly, she walked towards him, her face gleaming with happiness.

On reaching her, he held her close and kissed her tenderly and she whispered, 'I'm so glad you've come.'

He could only nod, words failed him; emotion having robbed him momentarily of his power of speech. They walked hand-in-hand, at ease with each other, their mutual affection as clear as the blue sky above. Outside the airport building he quickly hailed a taxi.

'Nyali Beach Hotel, upesi asante,' Tubs laughingly shouted at the young driver.

They sat in the back of the taxi, gazing into each other's eyes, as the taxi sped through the wide, palm-lined streets of Mombasa and then onto the golden sands of Nyali. They arrived within minutes at The Nyali Beach hotel, set amidst acres of tropical gardens, lovingly cared for, each acre a riot of colour and flowers of every variety. Tubs booked into his room overlooking the sea, with a balcony where coloured lizards played and chased one another in the sunlight.

'Let's go for a swim,' suggested Layla.

They made their way past the crowded swimming pool, though the gardens and onto the pure white sand of Nyali beach. This, thought Tubs is what heaven must be like. They swam together for half an hour, diving to peer at the thousands of angelfish which were constantly searching for food on the warm seabed.

Afterwards, their bodies glistening in the sun, they lay on the beach until the mid-afternoon heat drove them to the shade of the pool bar and a snack of fresh prawns and salad. Tubs felt a mixture of sickness and pain come over him as he sat Layla down and, as calmly as he could, told her his 'end of service' date. She looked sad but resigned and for a while neither of them spoke as the realisation of how this would affect their lives began to sink in. They returned to the beach to soak up the last hours of sun before retiring to Tubs' room to change. He had ordered in advance for dinner, barbecued beef in tamarind sauce, a Nyali speciality.

Suddenly, Layla announced, trying to inject a jocular atmosphere, 'Tomorrow, we must go to Malindi.'

'What a great idea,' Tubs replied, and catching her by the hand, walked her down to dinner.

They ate by candlelight and Tubs looked longingly at Layla, brimming with youthful health and beauty. After dinner they sat outside on the balcony and sipped Kenya Cane, a lethal concoction but smooth, the taste for it easily acquired. Just before midnight he hailed a taxi for Layla and after a long goodnight kiss she left, promising to be back at 0800 and ready for departure to Malindi.

Tubs awoke with a start and for a minute could not remember where he was. Staring at the large fan in the ceiling he panicked and leapt out of the bed, striking his toe on the marble floor. The air filled with obscenities until on reaching the hotel's mini bar he tore the top of a can of White Cap, and commenced to guzzle the contents in a crazy reasoning to ease the pain of his foot. Just before 0800 Layla arrived, carrying a large wicker picnic basket, and they boarded the service bus and sped off along the coast road to Malindi.

Over the years, Malindi had undergone periods of great prosperity compared with other East African coastal towns, but also periods of poverty. However, it still retained the charm and character of a bustling Arab township.

It was only a short journey and soon they alighted outside the Palm Beach Hotel. The streets were thronged with people buying carvings, basket-ware and colourful bead necklaces, many locally produced. From one of the stalls he bought a bag of *helwa*, the sweet-tasting local Turkish delight, which Layla ate with relish. At one of the many bars they stopped to quench their thirst and there Tubs noticed a blackboard on which was scrawled almost illegibly, 'One hour boat trips'.

'Let's go,' he shouted, taking Layla's hand and walking in the direction of the arrow on the blackboard. The next trip departed in thirty minutes, so deciding to have an early lunch, they sat down on a nearby bench and Layla produced a mixture of sandwiches and spicy curry samosas, one of his favourite snacks.

Soon four more passengers arrived and they all waited patiently whilst the young African boatman refuelled the outboard engine. Soon, and with a cheery wave of his hand, he beckoned his six passengers aboard. They set off at speed, the glass-bottomed boat making a huge bow-wave as it cut through the white surf. Soon they stopped and an anchor was thrown overboard. The young African hurriedly produced a bag, from which he threw fish feed into the water, and instantly thousands of fish became visible through the glass floor of the boat as they ate the titbits in the sea below.

Again the boatman threw the titbits over the side of the boat and the response was even more magical, with more varieties of fish arriving to claim their share of the free food. The boatman produced six pairs of goggles and the boat passengers quickly stripped down to their swimming attire, and one by one eased themselves over the bow and into the water for a memorable underwater experience. It was a world filled with silence, colour and every species of tropical fish imaginable. Layla had extensive experience, having been diving from an early age, and she took Tubs' hand as if instructing a child in a new technique.

Soon the boatman restarted the engine and they climbed back aboard, weary but happy after their exertions. The boat made its way back to the wooden quay at full speed, and the smiling boatman was paid, plus a generous tip.

Layla held Tub's hand, saying simply, 'Enjoyed yourself?'

'Immensely,' was the only word he could mouth to describe the pleasure of his day.

'Let's go back to Mombasa,' she said, catching hold of his hand and steering him in the direction of the bus queue.

With smoke pouring from the exhaust the old bus made its way along the long straight road into Mombasa, and as they descended from the top deck of the bus Layla whispered,

'My house is only a few blocks from here and we can have a drink.'

Carrying the now empty hamper and holding tight to Layla's slim waist, Tubs soon found himself at the front door of Layla's house, the sweet smell of the flowers from the garden filling his nostrils.

'Where's your mother?' queried Tubs.

'She's gone to Eldoret to visit her cousin,' was the quick reply.

The house smelt of jasmine and freshly-cut flowers, and, at peace with the world, they sat down on the two-seater sofa and drank chilled wine, the only sound being that of the crickets in the garden. He looked at Layla as if hypnotised and almost in a trance, lifted her up from the sofa, carried her into the bedroom, and lay her gently on the bed.

After removing his shirt he began to kiss her passionately on the neck and lips, and then, removing her bra, continued to use his lips to kiss and caress her brown breasts, as if measuring their fullness with his mouth. Slowly, she undid the buckle of his belt and pulled his khaki shorts to the ground. Removing her dress and panties she lay naked, still wearing her white high-heeled shoes. Slowly they fondled each other's bodies, lovingly and simply, as foreplay for genuine lovers always is.

But suddenly, despite the passion of the moment and his love for Layla, his carnal desire began to ebb away and, try as he might, his penis remained like a sail without any wind.

'Christ,' he thought, 'I'm impotent.'

Young and impatient, he felt cheated and a selfish thought flashed through his tortured brain.

'Is this how she will remember me?'

He lay back, his eyes full of sweat and the salt smarting, feeling drained, mentally and physically.

Layla kissed his chest and consoled him.

'It's alright my darling, it's alright, don't worry,' her words of comfort falling like rain in the desert.

He gasped for breath as the feeling of abject failure racked his body. His mind wandered to his home in England, his tedious, mentally fatiguing job in the accountants' dusty office, and of walking rain-lashed streets under a leaden sky. He wanted none of this, but as he looked at Layla he wondered how could it be her lot to be so unlucky as to fall in love with an airman far from home and only leased to this sun-kissed land before flying off into the sunset, surely never to be seen again?

God, how he hated himself for what he had done and what he was doing, and he wondered if it was the hand of God that had struck him impotent to teach him a lesson.

He rose unsteadily to his feet.

'Don't go my darling, stay here,' she implored, holding his hand to stop him moving away from the bed.

'I'd love to, if that's what you want,' he whispered simply.

He lay down beside her again and they held each other like two babies, comforting each other. Sleep did not come easily for either of them, with Tubs tossing and turning in an effort to ease the worrying thoughts that raced through his mind.

At dawn Layla sprang from the bed like a young gazelle and cooked a typical Kenyan breakfast, fresh mango as starters, followed by gammon, eggs, and the large brown buns, *muhamri*. It was delicious and for the first time for many hours Tubs felt happier.

They sunbathed in the small garden and wondered at the abundance of bougainvillea climbing the walls of the house, its brilliant colours of purple, red and orange eager to grow with or without the help of rain.

Living nearby was a young, fat Asian and as Tubs watched him striding towards his Mercedes, his gold watch shining in the sunlight. He wondered if Layla would, in the end, succumb to one of the many Asians, so powerful in East African commerce. Who could blame her for making the best of her life in this cynical world?

Shaking himself physically to dispel this depressing thought, he suggested a walk down to the local Tangana mosque. The main hall contained ablutions, where shoes were discarded and feet carefully washed before entering and praying to the quibble, the recess facing Mecca. After a short walk, both now in a silent mood, they reached the mosque, and after a brief washing ceremony entered the huge door into the serenely quiet and cool temple of prayer. They stood there, holding hands for a few moments, savouring the peace and tranquillity of the setting.

Leaving the mosque, now spiritually uplifted and in a more positive frame of mind, Tubs had the urge to buy Layla a new dress and pushed her through the doorway of the first Indian shop in Kilindini Road. Row upon row of dresses awaited her and her eager eyes showed her delight at the surprise. As if realising the urgency of the occasion she quickly chose a brown dress, and Tubs, without a hint of haggling, paid the shopkeeper his price.

'I'll wear it tonight for you,' she smiled.

They stepped into the street and were soon taxi-borne, and approaching the palm-tree lined entrance to Nyali.

They returned to Tubs' room, which offered panoramic views of the Indian Ocean and of a Dutch freighter, still lying on its side after running aground in a tropical storm some years ago.

25. *Farewell to Kenya*

Tubs took his time dressing for dinner, determined to make this a night they would both remember for the rest of their lives. Taking Layla by the hand, he led her down the long staircase to the dining room.

They ate slowly, soaking up the atmosphere and the air of festivity of the happy diners. After a couple of bottles of wine they took to the dance floor, holding each other close as the magic of Africa swept over them, enhancing their deep affection for each other still further.

For the first time Layla spoke of her family, of her brother who lived in Eldoret and of the death by consumption of her father at an early age. She poured out her life, chapter after chapter, page after page, as if baring her soul and emphasising her love to the man who sat opposite her. Soon it was midnight, the band fell silent and Tubs paid the bill and headed for the main hall and a taxi to Layla's house. He looked at his watch and a shiver of fear shot through his spine.

Time was not on his side. In flying parlance he was now 'on countdown' – the few days before the flight when the manifest was made up – and he knew for sure that his name would be on this list.

Arriving at Layla's house, even the crickets seemed noisier as the couple crept through the darkened doorway. They silently undressed and embraced each other. Layla's crisp white sheets crackled as he lay down beside her and she whimpered like a puppy as he kissed her breasts, lovingly.

But once again he was overcome by emotion that deprived him of his sexual drive. He held her like a child might hold a favourite teddy bear, frightened that it might be taken away. They lay in each other's arms until the luminous dial of his watch read 0630.

Outside the dawn was being orchestrated by a number of small birds nesting in the garden trees, which startled him into action. Feeling him move, Layla awoke, the whites of her eyes glowing in the darkened room. He had plenty of time but did not wish to hurry his departure. Layla made her way to the small kitchen and, finding her there, Tubs put his arms around her tiny waist. At breakfast they sat together in silence, neither daring to speak. Slowly they washed and dressed to await the taxi, which Tubs had ordered the night before.

Dead on time, the friendly African taxi-driver arrived and they climbed into the back seat. Tubs took one last look at the house before the taxi moved away down the sandy road. Traffic was light and soon the windsock at Mombasa airfield, blowing gently in the morning breeze, came into view. They alighted, Tubs tipping the driver generously, and walked into the empty coffee lounge. Layla broke the silence.

'You will write to me, won't you?'

He nodded, and kissed her. Again silence reigned, with them both holding hands, the only other person in the huge lounge being the waitress, busily clearing tables. Soon, with a roar and a cloud of dust, the giant Beverley of No.30 Squadron landed and taxied in. First through the arrivals door was the Squadron Leader, who, on recognising Tubs, shouted, 'Take off in twenty minutes, my lad!' adding with a wicked smile, 'Got your African carvings then?'

'Yes thank you sir,' was the only reply Tubs could manage, trying to look cheerful.

'I'll have to go, my love,' he said, picking up his holdall. He kissed her again and held her as tight as he could.

'Don't forget to write,' she implored.

'Of course I will,' he whispered, his lip quivering.

After one long, last passionate kiss he turned and walked through the door and across the tarmac to the awaiting aircraft. The No.1 engine was already commencing its start-up. He looked back and saw her waving. He could not see her face, but he knew that she was crying. He waved and shouted above the roar of the engine.

'I'll never forget you my love,' and with one final wave he climbed the steps into the passenger area of the Beverley, and strapped himself in for take-off.

The Beverley began to move, taxiing quickly to the holding position on the apron, and with no other air traffic it immediately accelerated, reached take-off speed rapidly, and climbed steeply out of Mombasa.

The Beverley ran into turbulence, dropping uncomfortably in a downdraft, but Tubs knew that this was not the reason for the knot in his stomach. He sat with his head down, feeling empty, and sadness washed over him in waves.

Suddenly, tears welled in his eyes and splashed like raindrops on the aircraft floor.

His emotional farewell to Layla had left him feeling drained and subdued. Next day he wrote to her, a long letter explaining his feelings for her and Kenya, enclosing a photograph. Dickie tried hard to cheer him up, buying him drinks and telling him how great it would be to be back in the UK. How could Tubs tell him that he did not want to go back to the UK? That he wanted, more than anything, to stay in Kenya with Layla, and that he could think of no other life?

Arriving early at the Orderly Room he heard the Adjutant bark, 'Ryan, come in here.'

'Christ,' he thought, 'what the hell has happened now?'

He dashed into the Adjutant's office to hear the him say, 'I didn't realise how long you'd been here, Ryan, but next Monday you go back to the UK for demob. Pleased?

He handed Tubs a large envelope containing his posting documents.

'Yes Sir, but you've been very good to me and I'll miss Kenya,' was the honest reply.

He hurried from the Orderly Room, clutching his posting documents, and went in search of Dickie.

'I go back to the UK on Monday,' he shouted through the Ops Room window, where his friend was busy chinographing the flight board.

'We'll get pissed tonight on the strength of it!' yelled Dickie.

Tubs hastily wrote home and another long letter to Layla. As promised, that night he and Dickie drank long and hard as Tubs saw the sands of Africa time running out. He had just two more days to serve at RAF Eastleigh, and for all official intents and purposes he had already left, as his 'blue chit' had been signed by every NCO i/c section, his uniform was packed and he now walked the camp in civilian clothes.

He wrote home, telling his parents he was on a flight via Istanbul and Rome and that he would telephone them on arriving in the UK. He telephoned Layla, and in a strained voice promised to write regularly from the UK. Sunday night was to be his last visit to the West Site NAAFI and to the bars downtown. To his surprise, Christopher the African tea-boy seemed genuinely sorry that he was leaving and he promised to write. He brought a smile from the big African's face by saying, 'Give those young sisters of yours my love,' recalling their flight to Kisumu. With little to do, Tubs walked aimlessly around the sections shaking hands and sying his goodbyes to his many acquaintances and friends

It seemed strange to be walking around as a civilian amidst a sea of airmen in blue uniform and he felt suddenly out of place. The NAAFI bar was full of a recent influx of recruits from the UK – known as 'moonies' due to the paleness of their skins. Wing Commander Taylor, although on leave, telephoned to wish him luck in the UK.

The ATC boys shook his hand with gusto and finally, finding the Adjutant, Flight Lieutenant Binedell, he said simply,

'Well Sir, I'll be off. Thanks for everything.'

The old South African eyed him sympathetically.

'I hope you've enjoyed the experience. If you ever get to Jo'burg look me up, I'm in the telephone book.'

Finally, he went down to Nairobi and bought Layla a parting present, asking the jeweller to send it on.

The dawn came up on his last day at RAF Eastleigh and in Kenya, his flight being confirmed as leaving Embakasi at midnight. With little to do, he hailed a taxi and alighted at the New Stanley Grill, spending a couple of hours talking to the barman, wishing him well when the day of Independence finally came. The bar girl at the San Chicaye gave him a big kiss and an offer of more, but he declined, giving his tight schedule as an excuse. He left the bar and walked the hot streets, alone and sad.

'Cheer up, you bastard!' he said aloud to himself.

He reminded himself that shortly he would be free from the constricting RAF uniform and be able to savour the delights of UK civilian life. He filled his mind with thoughts of Chester races and English beer and his morale improved. Hailing a taxi, he arrived back at Eastleigh and partook of high tea.

He had paid the dhobi-boy two weeks' money and also given him shoes, ties and trousers, with which he was obviously delighted. Christopher the Orderly Room tea-boy had always admired Tubs' RAF issue tropical sunglasses and on the last day he ceremoniously took them off and presented them to the cheerful African. He tried to think positively, but found his mind fearful of what the future held in store.

After buying a crate of Tusker he carried it to the billet as a gift for his pals, but this lasted but a few minutes and Dickie sent a message to the barman to deliver three more! The atmosphere was noisy, full of National Servicemen swapping tales of adventure and at 2100 hours Dickie stood on a table, clutching a beer glass and unsteadily announced,

'This is to Tubs Ryan, one of the best mates I've ever known.' He slapped Tubs heartily on the back, adding 'We're all coming to Embakasi to see you off.'

Tubs picked up his flight bag and walked the short distance to Air Movements, the African moon shining down brightly as if to highlight his departure. Checking in at Air Movements he joined his fellow passengers on the BUA flight, many of whom were families returning to the UK after having completed a full tour.

They climbed aboard the MT bus and soon the lights of Embakasi airport came into view, where the BUA Britannia was awaiting them, its livery gleaming like an askari's boots.

After entering the lounge, the passengers were called up in rank order and Tubs waited patiently for his turn. Some time went by before the short Air Movements Corporal yelled 'SAC Ryan!' and he walked forward, took his boarding card and headed towards the aircraft.

Suddenly, from the viewing platform, a throng of voices erupted in unison, shouting, 'Goodbye Tubs!'

He looked up and waved one last farewell before climbing the steps to the aircraft.

The smiling air hostess, fresh as a daisy in mid summer, stood at the door to greet him.

'Had a good tour sir?' she inquired.

'*Safari mzuri*,' he replied, with a wry smile, his eyes moist with emotion.

With a growl the jet-turbine engines accelerated and as the aircraft climbed steeply out of Embakasi through the dark Kenyan sky, the ground, and a large part of his life, slipped slowly away…

~ End ~

Glossary

askari:	Kenyan policeman or soldier.
bibi:	young female, woman.
chai:	tea.
duka:	any general store.
hapana mzuri:	no good.
jambo:	hello.
kwaheri:	goodbye.
mzuri sana:	good one.
PFO:	physical fitness officer.
pit:	bed.
raffiki:	friend.
Swahili:	language used in Central Africa to communicate between different tribes.
SSQ:	Station Sick Quarters.
SATCO:	Senior Air Traffic Control Officer.

Another book of interest from Woodfield

A Beat Around the Bush by Alastair Tompkins. The unusual and often hilarious experiences of a former officer in the **Kenya Police Force** 1953-1963. Price £12.95

In 1953 Alastair Tompkins left the UK to take up a post in **Kenya** – still a British Colony at the time – as one of a contingent of young British officers recruited to swell the ranks of the **Kenya Police Force**, their mission to combat the activities of the Mau-Mau terrorists, whose attacks on European-owned farms had made headline news around the world.

Home to a multi-ethnic population of Africans, Asians and Europeans and boasting some of the most spectacular scenery and wildlife in Africa, Kenya was an exotic and fascinating place compared to the drab post-war Britain Alastair had left behind... and he was soon to discover that police work in this colourful East African state would present him with many new and unexpected challenges.

Over the following ten years his duties would bring him into contact with a cast of colourful characters at every level of Kenyan society and thrust him into all manner of extraordinary situations – from the hair-raising to the outright hilarious – that only a policeman could experience.

In a perceptive and good-humoured narrative which succeeds in being both entertaining and informative Alastair describes his many experiences and brilliantly recaptures the spirit of those far-off colonial days, providing a valuable insight for those of us not fortunate enough to have witnessed them at first-hand and a nostalgic trip down memory lane for all fellow ex-colonials.

This high-quality softback is illustrated with numerous photos from the period, many in colour.

Purchase online at www.woodfieldpublishing.com